Maintaining Emotional Sobriety During COVID-19

Transforming Trauma into Post-Traumatic Growth

Tian Dayton, PhD, TEP

Library of Congress Cataloging-in-Publication Data
is available through the Library of Congress

978-0-9992320-6-4

High Watch Recovery Center
62 Carter Road, P.O. Box 607
Kent, Connecticut 06757

Cover photo ©Mexitographer

*This book is dedicated
with gratitude to and praise for
the health care workers on
the front lines and the mental
health practitioners.*

"It's not that we have lost our sense of certainty. We've lost our illusion of certainty! We never had it to begin with. This could be extremely unsettling, or amazingly liberating. This tiny virus of 125 nanometers has sent the entire world into chaos. (A nanometer is one billionth of a meter!)

All of our plans are up in the air. Markets are going crazy. Entire countries shutting down. And we have no clue what the future holds.

But that is always the case. We never know what the future holds. We only think we do. And we keep getting surprised when things don't turn out the way we expected.

Now the mask is off. We have to admit our vulnerability.

What will happen next?

We don't know. Our experts don't know. Our leaders don't know.

Only G-d knows. And that is the point. Only G-d knows!

Close your eyes and feel the uncertainty, make peace with it.

Let yourself be taken by it. Embrace your cluelessness.

Because in all the confusion there is one thing you know for sure.

You are in G-d's hands.

Keep calm.

Panic and fear are also contagious!

Take every precaution as advised by health authorities.

Wash your hands well. And every time you do,

Remember whose hands you are in."

Rabbi Morse
from Louise Stanger's email

Emotional Sobriety Graph

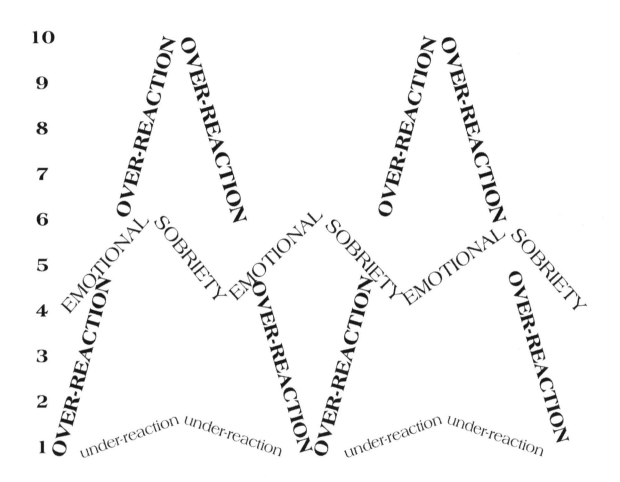

©Tian Dayton, PhD, TEP. Maintaining Emotional Sobriety During COVID-19.

Contents

# Acknowledgments

I wish to acknowledge you and those with whom you are bonding together, you are going through something unusual that will likely impact the rest of your life. I pray that it will have many hidden silver linings for you, those you love and the world we share.

I wish to acknowledge those health care professionals who are in the front lines, you are the most courageous among us and we salute and thank you. I understand that there will be some trauma-related issues that will possibly come into play, I wrote this workbook to try and support you in that, there is excellent research on these subjects. We know a lot that can help.

I also join hands with all of my wonderful colleagues in the mental health field who, to a person, are scrambling to give help while it is needed in order to avoid problems later. This is what we are trained to do and what many of us feel are meant to do. I am so touched by the devotion and creativity we're all sharing and the support we're giving each other as we stretch the bounds of our profession. It is an honor to be among all of you, you are my respected colleagues and my treasured friends.

And to Lawna Oldfield, a big thank you for jumping on this and staying on it so that we could turn it around as fast as possible, your clean and pleasing look is just what gives the user the graphic space to enter into the process and make it their own. Thank you for being my teammate in this!

And thank you to Larissa Henoch of Health Communications for her design of The Wheel of Self-Medication and the Emotional Sobriety Graph, generous as always.

And to Riyas Muhammed, my web developer from vDroid company and technical professional of so many hats, thank you for being so steady and reliable and for figuring out how to do absolutely anything that is needed, I cannot tell you how much I appreciate your diligent and intelligent work!

And I want to extend warm-hearted gratitude and appreciation for the leadership of Patty Evans, Sean Walsh, Carrie Steffensen, and the talented Wendy Ahlrichs from The Meadows Behavioral Healthcare. From the beginning they were working to make the best use possible of the significant resources at The Meadows in order to share expertise and knowledge that could be useful to our community at this moment in time and to make sure that there was no break for being able to get safe help when needed in this crucial period. You are inspiring to work with.

And lastly a big thank you to Jerry Schwab President/CEO of High Watch and Jess Colin Green Program Director/Associate General Counsel for seeing this pressing need and jumping in to publish this to address it. And to Samantha Quinlan, Director Innovations in Recovery whose ability to weave programs and people is inspiring, for putting it all together.

Introduction

It is one of life's paradoxes that sometimes the worst circumstances can bring the best out of us. According to the Adverse Childhood Experience (ACE) studies led by doctors Robert Anda and Vincent Felitti, at Kaiser Permanente's Health Appraisal Clinic in San Diego, we will all experience four or more serious life stressors that may be traumatizing, and according to positive psychology research, most of us will grow from them. So resilient qualities are not only what we're born with but also the strengths that we build through encountering life's challenges and developing the personal and interpersonal skills to meet them.

Post-traumatic growth (PTG), a phrase coined by Drs. Richard Tedeschi and Lawrence Calhoun—editors of *The Handbook of Post-Traumatic Growth*—describes the positive self-transformation that people undergo through meeting challenges head on. It refers to a profound, life altering response to adversity that changes us on the inside as we actively summon the kinds of qualities like fortitude, forgiveness, gratitude, and strength that enable us to not only survive tough circumstances but also thrive.

Today we're living through uncertain times. Even before the COVID-19 crisis, uncertainty around climate change, for example, was increasing. Since the advent of the 24-hour news channel, the amount of information we're exposed to daily is pounding away at our sense of a safe and secure future. We hear the same news over and over and over again. And because there is competition among news channels, headlines are designed to actually provoke the kind of cliff hanger anxiety that will get us to tune in. All of this was already creating significant *anticipatory anxiety* in our culture.

And now the uncertainty of the COVID-19 crisis is a clear and present danger; it's no longer out there in the future somewhere, it's here, now. We're having restrictions imposed on us that we have never experienced before. We fear both the present and the future. The shock is wearing off and we're adjusting to a new normal.

As weeks stretch on through our current challenge, we start to wonder when normal will return. The speculation is all over the place, as are the recommendations. This speculation can make us feel a quiet sense of despair. *Will life ever get back to normal? Will I feel safe again just going to the grocery store? What happened to my life, and when will I get it back?* Uncertainty is one of our most difficult feelings to manage. We humans like to wrap our minds around things, we like to know what's going to happen.

Our routines during this crisis are turned upside down. The structures that we used to rely on to give our week shape and stability are topsy-turvy. We're limited in our movements. Maybe we feel trapped as our ways of keeping ourselves happy or distracted, whether wandering down the vegetable aisle in the grocery store, going out for a cup of coffee, popping over to the gym, or having dinner with friends, are feeling potentially dangerous. These activities that were woven into the fabric of our daily lives are beginning to feel less accessible. We have a sense of foreboding.

"We experience a fear of the invisible: COVID-19 can be anywhere, and our primary safe sense vision, eye sight, is absolutely useless" says Christophe Sauerwein MSc, MBA. "We cannot see our enemy, and more over, it can be carried by our kin, friend, neighbour. And our innate coping styles need modifying. We survived through social gathering, "strength in numbers." Now we're being told to "socially distance." However, evidence of our inborn yearning to connect has never been more clearly demonstrated than by countries sharing information at unprecedented rates and zoom suddenly becoming a lifeline.

Some of the factors that can make a situation feel traumatic are a feeling of a loss of an orderly and predictable world, sudden shocking events that are outside of the normal scheme of things and a feeling that you can't escape. Welcome to COVID-19. Another trauma engendering feature is if there is the feeling of helplessness, that no matter what you do you cannot change what is happening and make it unhappen, that nothing you do will make a difference. (van der Kolk 1985) This is where the twelve-step community, which has PhDs in dealing with upturned, unpredictable worlds where the rules are constantly changing, picked out the right anthem, the "Serenity Prayer." *God grant me the serenity to accept the things I cannot change, the courage to change the things I can and the wisdom to know the difference.* It is a good prayer for these COVID-19 days, too.

There is a weekend phenomenon, well known to psychologists, when things fall apart just a little. Weekends can be stressful because there is less structure to your day, which can mean that your…let's call it "usual level of anxiety" has lost its ordinary binders. That means the little things that you don't let surface during the week—maybe because you're in the workplace where they wouldn't be appropriate or you just don't have time to think about them—surface on the weekend. You're a bit more irritable; your temper is short; your mood takes a dip, but then your weekly routine sweeps you up again and moves you into another zone.

Enter enforced confinement via "social distancing" or sheltering in place and suddenly life becomes one long weekend. Days run into each other. We don't really have to get fully dressed, and our structures are feeling wobbly. If you're on your same work schedule from home, it is still a different schedule, a new way of operating, unless you always work remotely. While parts of that can feel novel and even like a welcome change, there are other parts that can feel overwhelming and immobilizing. Or you may feel guilty because you're doing pretty well. You may feel anxiety without your usual sanity breaks or the whole things may feel overwhelming and immobilizing.

The feeling of being trapped, of not seeing an escape hatch, can make a situation feel harder than it actually is, moment by moment. So during this

COVID-19 crisis, you might be dealing with understandable anxiety of the crisis itself, without the reassuring comfort of your regular routines.

Because these days provoke extra anxiety in us, we need to set up equally strong safeguards to keep ourselves sane and safe.

Some among us have very few choices and are in the front lines of this epidemic and we're woefully unprepared because those who are supposed to be in charge…well…dropped the ball. This doesn't add to anyone's sense of safety and security. These people will likely be forever changed. In some ways they will develop a kind of wisdom and inner strength that is rare, a "survivor's pride" that comes from the knowledge that they have met a great challenge and handled it. They are heroes assuming they are among those who survive. They will likely feel stronger, more resilient and appreciative of life and relationships. In some ways they will have some mopping up to do of the parts of themselves that inevitably went on hold as they triaged responsibilities towards others. Some of those parts may be physical, for example did they eat well or grab whatever was handy which can of course affect their health, weight and sense of physical well-being. Some of those parts will be psychological and emotional, how did being in the front lines of one of the most out of control moments in our history and being the people to have to face it head on without proper protection and support, make them think and feel and how does this affect their world view and their experience of themselves on the inside and in their relationships?

But sheltering in place, living with uncertainty, physically distancing from those we love and our social and professional networks comes with significant challenges as well. Mental health workers who are on Zoom are talking about fatigue as they create tele-health alternatives for one-to-one and group therapy in order to address the needs of those experiencing anxiety, depression, suicidality and in some cases, relapse into addiction. Those on duty in treatment centers are on the front lines of mental health. Entrepreneurs are going lean and digital; small businesses are looking at viability and bankruptcy, and workers are being furloughed and fired. The list goes on. Parents are on full time childcare duty and, in addition, are actually becoming their children's teachers, another full-time job. The stresses on parents have led to greater amounts of alcohol consumption, other types of addictions and child abuse. They have also led to families pulling together and facing this challenge as a team and to children feeling happy and safe because they are seeing more of their parents than previously.

There is something called pre-trauma stress. "It's a phenomenon," writes Stacy Colino in US News and World Report, "you won't find in the Diagnostic and Statistical Manual of Mental Disorders, (DSM-V)....The symptoms are similar to post-traumatic stress disorder (including grief, sadness, worry, disturbing intrusive thoughts, sleep troubles and nightmares, and avoiding situations or activities that are reminiscent of the stressful event) but in this case, they stem from anticipatory anxiety about an event that may occur in the future." Parents can feel it on behalf of their children, "will they fall behind at school, will missing major life events wound them permanantly, do they yearn for their friends, their life?" Or we can feel it on our own behalf, "when will I have my life back?

Many of us will emerge from this COVID-19 period with trauma symptoms that, if we don't attend to them, could become PTSD. But this need not be you. And here is why. The way that you manage and see these days will be a significant factor in whether or not they become traumatizing, the little things you do *now*, can make a big difference *later*. How you set up your life during COVID-19, will impact how it affects you now, and how it will impact you in the months to come.

Maintaining Your Emotional Sobriety

Emotional sobriety allows us to live in 4, 5 and 6 rather than to shoot from 0–10 and 10–0, with no speed bumps in between. It is about *self-regulation*.

A hallmark of trauma is living in emotional and psychological extremes. Shooting from shut down to overwhelm and overwhelm back to shut down. Trauma invariably leads to a loss of *self-regulation*.

Self-regulation is a hallmark of emotional sobriety, so this workbook is about working with the parts of us that we have thrown out of concious awareness either because we were terrified at the time something happened and so our capicity to think about it or "observe" what was happening was off line, because the prefrontal cortex wah shut down.

When we're terrified or highly stressed, our thinking mind shuts down while our limbic system, our fight/flight/freeze system, revs way up. Nature didn't want us thinking about whether or not to run from a charging mammoth, she wanted us to flee for safety or to prepare for defending ourselves or to feign death until danger passed. That's why this is called our survival system. *Because the limbic system processes emotions, and sensory impressions like sights, sounds, smells and so forth, our body busily records our sense impressions during these moments of high stress, alongside the emotions we experienced. However, we made no overall meaning or interpretation of events, no story line.* We remember the general outline and what we associate with these incidences but not the details. Because our thinking mind, our pre-frontal cortex shuts down, we lose some of our exective function, which means our ability to name, refelct on and regulate our emotions through understanding is compromised. So later, when something scares or stresses us again, the feelings of fear, vulnerability or anxiety can trigger these "frozen memories, these body memories" inside of us but our reasoning is missing unless we develop specific skills of mindfulness like learning to "pause" and "reflect." And because the limbic system also processes bonding chemicals, when we're traumatized it affects our relationships and our ability to trust and attach. Trauma can make us feel different, it's de-personalizing so it can lead to isolating which can lead to depression and we don't effectively use our relationships as part of our self-regulation. We feel depending maybe isn't such a good idea. So when we get triggered, we self-protect, we slide into survival responses of fight, flight or freeze and we lose a sense of connection with the other person.

This is why I have made guided meditations and guided imageries a part of this process because they teach the skills of mindfulnes, self soothing, self awareness and self regulation in a relaxing and plesant way. I have also developed specific imageries for processing emotions mindfully, for developing emotional literacy.

So trauma is not only what happens to you but how you respond to it on the inside. Because we have not processed and understood our terror related memories, they remain unconscious and they have to emerge as symptoms like intrusive thoughts, nightmares, anxiety, body aches, depression or a desire to self-medicate.

Becoming Aware of Our Triggers: Separating the Past from the Present

To maintain self-regulation, you need to develop the ability to process rather than shut down feelings, to understand your inner world rather than push it away. Otherwise, when you get triggered, your hidden or unprocessed emotions will likely jettison to the surface and come out as blame, anger, negativity, sadness or even rage. And because they were never thought through to begin with, they will look for a target and that target is likely to be whatever triggered them. Then the wounds of the past get mixed up with this current stressor, and we have a real mess to sort through.

But as we develop the ability to tolerate and "sit with" what we are feeling so that we can become more mindful of what it is going on inside of us, we become a witness in our inner world. And we also want to develop what the Buddhists call *self-compassion;* we want to go easy on ourselves and in turn lighten up on others. Because if you enter this COVID-19 period with adverse childhood experiences, and have never delved down to understand how you got hurt and how feeling unseen and wounded affected you, you are likely to get triggered back into the wordlessness of early, childhood pain and you'll feel at risk and alone, all over again.

Journaling Our Emotions

Journaling is actually a very helpful way of dealing with unfelt feelings. As we abandon ourselves to the paper, feelings come pouring out of us that we have forgotten were there, and as they do our thinking mind witnesses them, and once we can sit with them and tolerate their intensity without acting out, shutting down or self-medicating, a new narrative begins to take shape before our eyes. It helps to have journaling exercises that are focused and include the kinds of well researched inquiry that can help you to work through and normalize what you are experiencing. This is how you can use this experience as a moment of personal growth because frankly, the gold is in what gets triggered, what triggers us sends up a red flag marking the spot of hidden pain.

Once you can translate your hidden feelings into words, you will wonder what took you so long, because dealing with what you have gone to so much trouble to avoid feeling is liberating and energizing and a huge relief. We need to learn that we can survive our overwhelming feelings of anxiety and pain, and as we do something paradoxical happens, they become less overwhelming, they actually dissipate. And as we feel them, we develop strength, so that the next time we have to sit through our overwhelming feelings, it's easier. We experience a new kind of safety, a safety living in our own skin.

Creating Safety

It's very important to be proactive and institute the kinds of buffering basics into your day that keep you resourced, that reduce stress and build resilience. The supports that you put in place now can serve as safeguards to alleviate or lessen some of the unusual stress that could become cumulative. Setting up a schedule, a support network, and recovering a sense of safety, personal space, and quiet, can help you to avoid falling into the kinds of problems that could worsen over time.

Here are some practical ways to do that:

✦ **Put a mental boundary around this period.** Understand that this will not go on forever. Even though there is uncertainty, there will be a beginning, middle, and an end to the COVID-19 crisis.

✦ **Create a sense of safety in your home.** You need a safe haven, a pleasant and orderly world, a predictable schedule for your days. Make your life at home as pleasant as possible in whatever ways are meaningful to you. Have an orderly, comfortable work space, create reassuring routines and daily rituals. Maintain order in your personal world. It counters the feeling of helplessness to take charge of your environment.

✦ **Stay Connected and Resourced:** We have ways of remaining connected to those we love that are unprecedented. We can email, text and FaceTime those we love. We can share pictures and films of how and what w're doing. We can FaceTime and actually see and visit each other in real time. We can work, do group therapy and gather informally on zoom. Though we're isolating physically, we can stay connected emotionally and often professionally. Grant H. Brenner, writes in a recent issue of Psychology Today, that social media may actually be increasing our ability to tolerate uncertainty and isolation thus facilitating post traumatic growth. And in any case, we can surmise that it can help to ameliorate pre-trauma symptoms.

✦ **Take it a day at a time.** Don't panic. Try seeing anxiety as a contagious virus of its own that can undermine your emotional health and the health of the systems that you're operating in. Take responsibility for your own state of calm.

✦ **Have a schedule:** Don't let time crowd you into a dark corner, take charge of your day. Organizing your time will give you a greater sense of control and will reassure you and all concerned, that much of life can still feel normal.

✦ **Maintain family, couple and personal rituals:** Rituals provide a sense of stability. You know what they are for you: a walk, exercise, a meeting, coffee in the am, morning meditation or inspiring reading, sitting down for lunch, nap, family time, you name it. Even choosing a movie to watch together, making popcorn and cuddling up on the couch can be a reassuring family activity that brings relaxation, pleasure and calm to everyone.

✦ **Find a project:** Engaging in a project that is a bit challenging but not too hard can help you to enter what Mihaly Chikszentmihalyi researched and calls a "flow state." Flow states, whether painting, golf, cleaning, writing, scrapbooking, etc., leave you feeling more whole, relaxed and integrated. They both stabilize and elevate your inner state. Do things that give you a sense of agency and control. Clean a cupboard, create something, journal, sew, do woodworking.

✦ **Eat a healthy diet.** Your body is your best friend and first line of defense when it comes to staying safe and healthy, treat it well and with love and respect. If you eat foods that are "empty calories" or do not give you the healthy fuel that you need to feel good or bog down your system trying to digest what shouldn't be in it in the first place, your physical and emotional immunity will suffer. Be aware that alcohol lowers physical immunity very significantly. Find alternative ways of relaxing. Cook lovely food, eat it slowly and enjoy it. Have a brown-bag Zoom dinner date or cocktails (healthy ones).

✦ **Breathe:** Remember to do rhythmic, diaphragmatic breathing, it will calm your nervous system and increase your sense of well-being. Take extra downtime; stress and uncertainty can be tiring, make sure that you relax when you can and find healthy ways of unwinding.

✦ **Exercise:** Exercise is always important, but as a way of managing stress, depression or anxiety, it is a must. The natural serotonin that your body releases through exercise is one of nature's most important mood stabilizers. According to studies at Duke, a brisk walk 3/4x/week is as effective for managing depression as medication! To say nothing of the obvious perks of being more fit and feeling great! This is so important for emotional as well as physical wellness.

✦ **Get extra sleep, relaxation and rest.** Stress is tiring and we're all under some if not a lot of stress. Extra rest can help to manage this and keep you in balance.

✦ **Get out into nature and fresh air as often as you can, it will soothe your soul.** Reconnect with the outdoors, listen to nature sounds, observe, walk, look around and appreciate all that is beautiful about the world we live in.

✦ **Stay Positive:** Watch your narrative, if you have a doom and gloom narrative try changing it to a "we'll all be fine if we pull together and keep our heads straight" This one is is a game changer; your attitude is up to you. No one can adopt a positive attitude for you, you owe it to yourself and to those close to you to stay positive.

✦ **Don't isolate:** Lean into your relationships, research is absolutely clear on this one, relationships are key in maintaining both emotional and physical health; we are pack animals; we need each other. Social isolation is only physical; you do not need to isolate from family and friends, thanks to technology. Keep in touch with the people in your life who matter to you.

✦ **Embrace the extra time you have as a result of physical distancing.** If you are spending more time with your family, make the most of it. Families that learn how to cope and get through things by pulling together are stronger for it. These experiences can be very bonding if you keep your heads and hearts in the right place.

✦ **Limit the time you talk about the virus.** (My daughter suggested this and finds that adopting this with her husband and family helps them to stay positive). Don't stare at the news channel all day, keep up on what you need to know then break away and do normal things.

✦ **Follow all safety recommendations from the CDC:** You do not need to figure this whole thing out, you just need to do your best with the information that's out there. Follow the recommendations of the experts you deem sensible and capable.

✦ **Take simple actions, stay out of collapse:** Collapse is a natural trauma response to feeling helpless but it leads to problems. Creating a schedule, putting things on paper, engaging in a project, organizing a meal or a family activity are all ways of bringing our thinking mind back on board again.

✦ **Learn about fight/flight/freeze and know when you're in it.**
When we get scared or overwhelmed our animal DNA tells us to run (or run mentally/dissociate), to fight (criticize, yell, get aggressive and me-first) or to freeze (shut down, withdraw). And our thinking mind shuts down as our limbic (read sensory and emotional) revs up, we become over-reactive. We need to find ways of calming down in our bodies and minds to maintain emotional sobriety and regulation. Yoga, deep breathing and meditation are great.

✦ **Do a spiritual reset.** Instead of getting lost in the feeling of uncertainty, reflect on the idea that all we really know about is today. COVID-19 puts us in touch with our own mortality. Depending on your spiritual leanings, it can also put you in touch with the part of yourself that feels eternal or your higher self. Moving into this space of the higher self is nourishing and revitalizing. When you learn to access this space within you at will, the situation may not change, but your perspective does.

✦ **Reassure those you love that you're doing well by taking the steps to take care of yourself.** If you are in a high-risk group, try not to be an extra burden for those who love you. If you're an older adult act with steadiness and maturity.

✦ **Play music, dance!** Be playful, play is a great stress reliever and a wonderful way to bond with family and friends.

✦ **Self Soothe:** Watch uplifting videos, they give us a shot of serotonin. Take a hot bath to get a shot of prolactin. Self sooth.

✦ **Maintain an attitude of gratitude.** Take notice of what's going right and think about it over and over again, *affirm what is beautiful in life.* Rest in gratitude.

✦ **Don't feel too Guilty:** If you're one of those people who is enjoying the change of venue, more family, couple or personal time, shorter (much) commute and the work variety you're experiencing, don't worry about it. You're lucky. The more people who feel happy, the better for everyone. Milk your good moments and feel them fully!

✦ **And finally, do not be perfect!!!** We're all slogging through this together, do the best you can, then forgive yourself for slipping— we're all slipping. Make being kind to yourself a priority and go easy on those around you. Stay safe and well, "this too shall pass."

The Italians who hung out the window during lockdown and sang together have seen much worse than this in their communities. They learned that pulling together rather than pulling apart gave them the spiritual nourishment to get through. Keep your eye on those who are pulling together and feel the goodness of it rather than on just what is going wrong. Keep a tally of the lessons you're learning and the world is learning, they are deep and they are real. Keep the big picture in mind, there will be life after COVID-19.

Where To Use This Book

As a personal Journal: This can be a "for my eyes only" intimate world in which you express your most personal and deep thoughts and feelings. It can be accompanied by extra journal pages on which you write more on the various topics you will find here. If you buy the kindle version, you can make notes on it, highlight text and do the journaling part on separate paper.

As one-to-one therapy or coaching: This can be used as a focus for therapy or coaching that outlines the issues that may arise during this COVID-19 period. Each client will have their own copy and can fill exercises in as homework that is shared and further processed at sessions.

In group therapy: Each group member and the therapist has this workbook. Exercises can be done at home and brought to the group to share or as part of the therapy together.

In peer support groups: If each member of the group has their own journal, exercises can be done between groups and then shared on zoom or other forms of "get togethers." After sharing exercises participants can continue to share around the issues being discussed.

In treatment centers or sober houses: The workbook can be used as a holding space for personal experience or exercises that can be done in the groups and then shared. The coloring of mandalas in the second half of this book also provide a wonderful group activity that not only is proven to significantly reduce anxiety, but is also a great way to learn to develop social skills and have sober fun.

On Zoom: Zoom fatigue is being experienced by therapists conducting groups and participants in groups. Using this workbook helps the group members to arrive warmed-up, focused and ready to explore what has been coming up for them throughout the week.

ADDITIONAL FREE SUPPORTS:
log onto *tiandayton.com/COVID-19 Supports*

Meditations and Guided Imageries: You will find guided imageries that you can listen to at home or in a group if you're in safe facilities together. They will help you to learn the skills of deep relaxation and emotional processing. They are also soothing and relaxing.

Film Clips: You will find some brief film clips that explain some of the concepts in the workbook that you can listen to at your convenience on your own or as a group in a safe space.

Psychodramas: Additionally, if you wish to see people doing psychodramas that explore some other life issues, you can find them by looking under "experiential therapies."

emotionexplorer.com: Another great resource for processing feelings is emotionexplorer.com on tiandayton.com. It's fun and engaging.

Mindfulness

Mindfulness and emotional sobriety are fundamentally linked. At the center of mindfulness is learning to witness the inner workings of our own thoughts and emotions, to witness, to watch, and to observe. This skill is fundamental to healing, and emotional sobriety. When we're in the here and now, what comes up from within is more evident and we see it through calmer and clearer eyes.

Mindfulness is inextricably connected to the breath. Even, rhythmical breathing will allow the nervous system and the mind to calm down.

Mindfulness will let you back up from an argument, breathe, take stock, and try a different approach. It will allow you to observe if you are moving toward a panic attack or a rage state.

Personally I experience my mind these days as sort of like a zoom screen that moves in and out of freezing. Generally I am able to maintain a pretty even flow but if I hear bad or frightening news, my mind freezes for a while or for short, intermittant moments, then normal movement resumes. It may do this repeatedly or just once in a while, depending on the severity of the news I hear. Mindfulness helps me to recognize when I am freezing up and to use my breath to unfreeze, relax, reconnect my mind with my body and return to the moment.

After an eight-week course in mindfulness, Tom Ireland reports in an article written for *Scientific American,* called "What Does Mindfulness Do for Your Brain?" (June 12, 2014), that these rather startling changes will happen. You will reduce the fight/flight center of your brain, actually shrinking the amygdala. As the amygdala shrinks, the prefrontal cortex thickens (who knew?). The "functional connectivity" between these regions—that is, how often they are activated together—gets weaker, while the connections between areas asso-ciated with attention and concentration get stronger.

The implications of this when it comes to trauma resolution are only too obvious. The amygdala, our fear center, down-regulates and sends fewer panic-type messages out to the body and mind, and our thinking mind gets stronger and is better able to hold and process experience and emotion, all of which leads to an enhanced ability to self-regulate. We're getting neurons to fire and wire together in the direction that is more conducive to happy living and calm interactions.

CHAPTER 1
Shock, Helplessness and Overwhelm

Stages of Personal Reactions
to the COVID-19 Crisis

Trauma Responses to COVID-19	Growth Inhibiting Responses	Growth Producing Responses
Shock	Denial Unsafe Behaviors	Fact Finding Assessing
Helplessness	Collapse Immobilization	Mobalizing Setting Up Systems Stockpiling
Overwhelm	Anxiety Panic	Resourcing Scheduling Connecting Online
Grief Sense of Loss Disconnection	Depression Anger Self Medication	Reaching Out Mindfulness Processing Emotions
Uncertainty	Wishful Thinking Acting Out	Simplifying Staying Positive Building Resilience
Fear of the Future Feeling Anxious and Scared	Down the Rabbit Hole PTSD	Present Oriented Growth Mindset Life on Life's Terms

© Tian Dayton, PhD, TEP. Maintaining Emotional Sobriety During COVID-19.

Where Are You Now?

Look over these stages, where do you feel you are now? For each stage, jot down two or more ways that stage has manifested for you in terms how you felt/feel, what you thought/think and how you act/acted. If where you are is in the Growth Producing Responses column, then enter those thoughts, feelings and behaviors. You can pass through these stages more than once or, in advance of their actually happening (in anticipation).

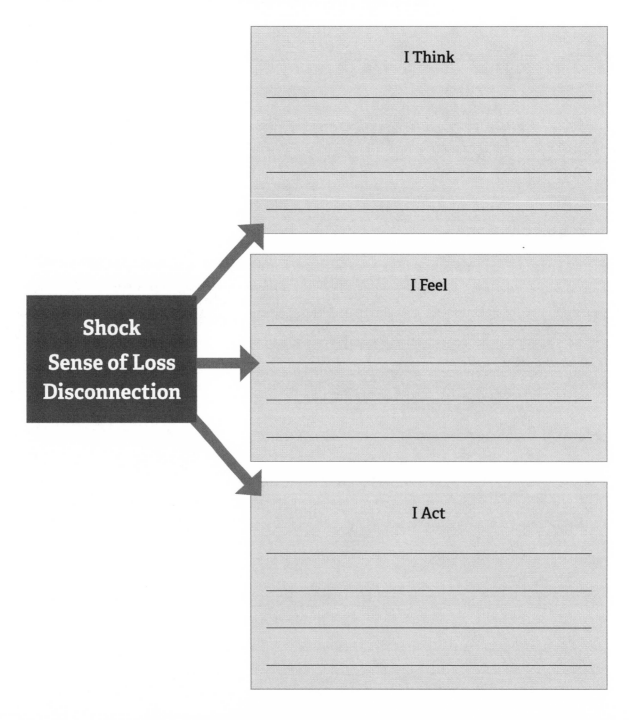

I Think

I Feel

**Shock
Sense of Loss
Disconnection**

I Act

I Think

_____

_____

_____

_____

_____

Helplessness

I Feel

_____

_____

_____

_____

_____

I Act

_____

_____

_____

_____

_____

_____

I Think

_____

_____

_____

_____

_____

_____

Overwhelm

I Feel

_____

_____

_____

_____

_____

_____

I Act

_____

_____

_____

_____

_____

_____

I Think

_____

_____

_____

_____

_____

_____

_____

Grief

I Feel

_____

_____

_____

_____

_____

_____

I Act

_____

_____

_____

_____

_____

_____

I Think

_____

_____

_____

_____

_____

_____

Uncertainty

I Feel

_____

_____

_____

_____

_____

_____

I Act

_____

_____

_____

_____

_____

I Think

_____

_____

_____

_____

_____

_____

I Feel

_____

_____

_____

_____

_____

_____

Fears of the Future

I Act

_____

_____

_____

_____

_____

_____

Pre-Trauma Symptom Floor Check

The exercise below is a way to explore the kinds of issues you're experiencing during the COVID-19 crisis. If you don't see the symptom you're experiencing, just write what you're feeling into the "other" box!

Which symptom is drawing you at the moment? Say a few words about how this feels or manifests for you.

_____

_____

_____

_____

_____

_____

Which symptom did you NOT feel before COVID-19, any wistfulness about life without it?

_____

_____

_____

_____

_____

Which one do you hide from other people, how does it feel to hide it?

_____

_____

_____

_____

_____

_____

Which feeling once it takes hold of you tends to have a life of its own?
Describe how that tends to manifest and how you feel as it does.

_____

_____

_____

_____

_____

When you're feeling this way, what's your self-talk? Do you have an inner
monologue? Can you write it out?

_____

_____

_____

_____

_____

When you're feeling this feeling what do you tend to do?

_____

_____

_____

_____

_____

What do you long to hear from someone else when you're feeling this way? What do you need or yearn for?

_____

_____

_____

_____

_____

What is the kindest, most reassuring thing you could say to yourself at these moments?

_____

_____

_____

_____

_____

What do you miss most about pre-COVID-19 days?

_____

_____

_____

_____

_____

_____

CHAPTER 2
Exploring Fears and Anxieties

Explore Your Fears and Anxieties

Nearly everyone uses this quote but that's because it's so good, "the only thing we have to fear, is fear itself." Franklin Delano Roosevelt said this and he ought to know. He had to learn to live with polio and he had to take our country through World War ll and rebuild it afterward. He was not only paralyzed by polio, but at one point in his life, he was paralyzed by his fear. He learned to face his fear and how not to allow his physical paralysis become an emotional and psychological paralysis. He set an example of what courage could accomplish and he led the world toward a better tomorrow and that tomorrow came.

Fear is a natural, knee jerk response, one that gets hardwired very quickly. It's adaptive and important. It's hanging onto fear, milking it, living it, catastrophizing it that is maladaptive. But as easily as we can be conditioned to feel fear (think rats and experiments) we can let fear go. Our fears can be deconditioned. Facing them head on, looking at them, questioning them and talking ourselves off of the ledge are all ways that we can make sure we don't let our fears get the better of us.

And there is another remarkable way that we can deal with fear and that is by living in the moment, by staying present, by asking ourselves the question, "what's the matter now, right now?" Much of our mental anguish consists of replaying old fears and complexes from the past or fearing the future. Once we have made responsible plans, obsessing about them won't help. Once we have understood and processed feelings from the past, ruminating won't help. This doesn't mean we lose our memories, it just means we learn to take a step back from causing ourselves unnecessary inner stress and pain.

The following exercise is a way for you to face your fears, to understand them better, to make friends with them.

Fear and Anxiety Floor Check

Panic

Phobias (social, agora-phobia, creepy crawlies, etc.)

Chronic regrets/ envy or feeling you have "missed out"

Overcontrolling, people, places, and things

Irrational fears or free floating anxiety

Hypervigilance/ always waiting for the other shoe to drop. Fear of panic attacks

Constantly feeling overwhelmed or under the gun

Somatic/Health Issues Somatization

Fear of retribution or punishment if life works out

Tightness in chest or muscles, back or headaches, body aches

Caretaking too much

Talking too much

Sleep issues

Other:

Glance over the squares and see what word or words draw you. Share about why you think they popped out at you.

_____

_____

_____

_____

What part of your body do you feel this feeling in? Describe the physical sensations, if any, that accompany the feeling.

_____

_____

_____

_____

How do you breathe at moments when you are feeling like this? Do you remind yourself to breathe or if not, what happens next? Do you stop breathing or shorten your breaths?

_____

_____

_____

_____

What situations trigger this feeling in you? And once the feeling is triggered, where do you go in your head?

_____

_____

_____

_____

Do you have images in your mind of how others see you at these moments? If so, what do you imagine others might be thinking?

_____

_____

_____

_____

Describe a situation in which you felt you managed this set of feelings well.

_____

_____

_____

_____

What fears come up for you around the COVID-19 crisis? Say a little about that.

_____

_____

_____

_____

If this feeling had a color what would it be?

_____

If this feeling had a smell what would it be?

_____

If this feeling had a shape what would it be?

_____

If this feeling had a sound what would it be?

_____

If this feeling had a texture what would it be?

_____

If this feeling had a taste what would it be?

_____

Have you ever felt these kinds of fears or something like them before? If so, can you talk about that?

_____

_____

_____

_____

Do you have fears of what might happen after the COVID-19 crisis? If so, what are they?

_____

_____

_____

_____

What can you do for yourself or say to yourself right now, that will let you feel better in this moment?

_____

_____

_____

_____

CHAPTER 3

Anger:
The Limbic Storm

The Anger Self-Check

Answer the following questions by placing a check (✓) in the box that best describes "where you are."

1. How much anger is COVID-19 creating in you?

   ○ *Almost none*   ○ *Very little*   ○ *Quite a bit*   ○ *Very much*

2. How triggered do you get around other people's anger?

   ○ *Almost none*   ○ *Very little*   ○ *Quite a bit*   ○ *Very much*

3. How much shame do you feel around your anger?

   ○ *Almost none*   ○ *Very little*   ○ *Quite a bit*   ○ *Very much*

4. How much do you beat yourself up when you get angry?

   ○ *Almost none*   ○ *Very little*   ○ *Quite a bit*   ○ *Very much*

5. How easily triggered are you, into an angry state?

   ○ *Almost none*   ○ *Very little*   ○ *Quite a bit*   ○ *Very much*

6. How much hurt do you think is underneath your anger?

   ○ *Almost none*   ○ *Very little*   ○ *Quite a bit*   ○ *Very much*

7. How depressed do you feel around your anger?

   ○ *Almost none*   ○ *Very little*   ○ *Quite a bit*   ○ *Very much*

8. How overtly aggressive do you become?

   ○ *Almost none*   ○ *Very little*   ○ *Quite a bit*   ○ *Very much*

9. How passive aggressive do you become?

    ○ *Almost none*   ○ *Very little*   ○ *Quite a bit*   ○ *Very much*

10. How much does your anger affect your intimate relationships?

    ○ *Almost none*   ○ *Very little*   ○ *Quite a bit*   ○ *Very much*

11. How much does your anger affect your work life?

    ○ *Almost none*   ○ *Very little*   ○ *Quite a bit*   ○ *Very much*

12. How good are you at dealing with your anger in healthy ways?

    ○ *Almost none*   ○ *Very little*   ○ *Quite a bit*   ○ *Very much*

13. How much fear do you feel around your anger?

    ○ *Almost none*   ○ *Very little*   ○ *Quite a bit*   ○ *Very much*

14. How much does your anger disrupt your life?

    ○ *Almost none*   ○ *Very little*   ○ *Quite a bit*   ○ *Very much*

Process Your Anger

Anger is a normal part of the grief process and can be part of uncertainty and confinement and COVID-19. On the pages that follow, let's take a deeper look at how your anger may be manifesting and how you can gain some clarity and balance around it. Anger that is turned inward, that remains unexpressed or even unfelt can morph into depression. Anger can also be used to cover up feelings of grief that make us feel vulnerable and like we're falling apart when we feel them. But the truth is, there is strength in vulnerability. When we can work with our anger and feel our grief, that state of frozeness and immobility that we experience as depression, can begin to move. We can create some space on the inside.

Part of creating resilience is changing a dark, angry and negative narrative into a more positive one. An uplifting narrative creates emotional and physical immunity. Negative thinking impacts our mood, our emotion and our physical health. It creates internal stress which leads to the release of cortisol in the body which can lead to inflammation; "inflammation is an important risk factor for depression and cardiovascular disease, which frequently accompany PTSD." An outcome conducted with people who had "hi hostility" scores in response to problems reported these findings in Psychological Medicine, Cambridge University Press (Psychol Med. 2016 Sep; 46(12): 2571–2582). Those "who developed an episode of PTSD or major depression reported poorer well-being, as measured by more days off work, greater sleep problems and burn-out, and lower quality of life at the 2-year follow-up than those who did not develop these problems during training. Those with an episode of PTSD were also more likely to report weight gain over the 2 years than those without PTSD." Another common outcome of PTSD is self-medication with drugs and alcohol (van der Kolk *et al.* 1986)

When we get angry, in a state of high stress, or locked into a negative narrative, our anger or negativity makes the current situation we're in very complicated to work through. When we remain stuck in anger, other emotions associated with the grief process, like sadness, hurt and a feeling of "falling apart" never emerge. We use anger to protect our feelings of vulnerability and it keeps us from exposing and processing the kinds of emotions that would help us to heal and grow.

The Angry Body

We experience anger in our bodies as well as in our minds, which is why it feels like it takes us over. When we get triggered into anger, our heart rate accelerates, our blood pressure rises, and our rate of breathing increases. Our body's muscles tense up. We suddenly feel all of these disquieting sensations surging through us, our face may flush as increased blood flows through our limbs to ready us to take evasive action or to fight. Along with increased blood flow, stress/energy hormones like adrenaline and noradrenaline are released in our brain/bodies that give us the burst of energy that's behind our knee-jerk desire to take immediate, self-protective action. Another very interesting thing happens that explains a lot about why angry people act the way they act, *our attention narrows and becomes locked onto the target of our anger; soon we can pay attention to nothing else.*

The same lingering arousal that keeps us primed for more anger, can also interfere with our ability to clearly remember details of our angry outburst. A certain level of arousal is vital for efficient remembering. As any student knows, it is difficult to learn new material while sleepy. Moderate arousal levels help the brain to learn and enhance memory, concentration, and performance. There is an optimal level of arousal that benefits memory, however when arousal exceeds that optimal level, it makes it more difficult for new memories to be formed. This is why it is difficult to remember details of really explosive arguments.

The Rage State: Hijacking Our Brains

Rage can hijack our brains, it can take us over, obliterating reason and blowing past ordinary boundaries. And we can be almost in a black- out which is why people who rage often don't remember what they were like while raging and they minimize their effect on others. "During rage attacks...those parts of the brain that are central to feeling and expressing anger, such as the amygdala and the hypothalamus, commandeer the rest of the brain. In this wholesale takeover, the cerebral cortex is overwhelmed, and restraint and reasoning are impossible.... Although rage—by which I mean anger that is extreme, immoderate or unrestrained—may be adaptive as a response to severe threat, in most situations it destroys much more than it accomplishes," says Dr. Norman Rosenthal in *The Emotional Revolution*. Chronic rage might also be an indicator of depression. It's been estimated that 40 percent of those suffering from rage attacks also suffer from clinical depression.

Sudden angry outbursts can also be a part of PTSD or unresolved grief. Rosenthal continues, "Dr. Martin Teicher and colleagues at Harvard have found that adults who were abused as children, whether verbally, physically, or sexually, show brain wave changes over the temporal lobe of the cerebral cortex. These changes resemble those seen in people with documented seizures in the temporal lobe, which surrounds the limbic structures.... Teicher suggests that early traumatic experiences might kindle seizure-type activity in this area, resulting in a storm of electrical activity in the emotional part of the cerebral cortex... the end result could be a brain that is cocked and all too ready to fire off a limbic storm." (Dayton 2019)

If anger has a physiological preparation phase during which our resources are mobilized for a fight, it also has a wind-down phase as well. We start to relax back toward our resting state when the target of our anger is no longer accessible or an immediate threat. It is difficult to relax from an angry state, however. The adrenaline-caused arousal that occurs during anger lasts a very long time (many hours, sometimes days), and lowers our anger threshold, making it easier for us to get angry again. Though we do calm down, it takes a very long time for us to return to our resting state. During this slow cool-down period we are more likely to get very angry in response to minor irritations that normally would not bother us.

Anger can hide under a lot of rocks, it can leak out under various disguises or burst forward, understanding the many ways in which anger can manifest is another way of helping us to understand and manage it more thoughtfully.

We have pretty much been taught that anger is a bad thing to express, which can make us imagine that it's bad to even feel it. But anger is actually very important. It gets a bad reputation because it can so easily get out of control and when it does, we can become nasty, cold, manipulative with no conscience and even abusive. But anger is also an important source of information to the self, it lets us know when we've been hurt and if our boundaries have been stepped on. Gaining some level of self regulation around our anger can be a game changer in our ability to be comfortable in our own skin and happy in our relationships. We become capable of intimacy that doesn't obliterate the boundaries and thus, self of another person while still making room for ourselves. There are few emotions that can more successfully knock a hole in your emotional sobriety more than anger but then, on the other hand, we probably don't ever become truly emotionally sober without learning to make friends with and regulate this very core emotion that tells us so much about where our inner boundaries lie. While anger can feel and in may ways be better than being stuck in a depressive state, it needs to be brought into consciousness and understood, it needs to be tamed. Feeling our anger and getting honest and humble about how it shows up in our lives is a first step in getting to know yourself and your own anger.

Anger Floor Check

Passive aggression

Whining Complaining

Cynicism

Negativity

Resentment

Self-medication

Criticism

Acting-out behaviors

Rage

Violence

Depression

Stonewalling

Withdrawal

Coldness

Shunning

Other:

Which form of anger is generally your "go to"? Say something about that.

_____

_____

_____

Which form of anger do you feel you manifest the most during this COVID-19 period? Say a bit about how, where or with whom it manifests.

_____

_____

_____

Which form do you have the hardest time with when you encounter it in others? Describe how it makes you feel or who or what period in your life it reminds you of.

_____

_____

_____

Which form of anger do you feel those around you have the hardest time with when they encounter it in you? How do you imagine they feel in your presence?

_____

_____

_____

Which manifestation of anger did you learn from the family you grew up in? Describe a scene or situation that pops into your mind.

_____

_____

_____

Who displayed this form of anger the most and how did it feel to you when they were in this state?

_____

_____

_____

What did those you grew up with do once they got angry, were they angry with you? Did they take responsibility for their anger? Did they apologize?

_____

_____

_____

What strategies do you feel are best received by others in your life? Do you own you anger? Do you apologize?

_____

_____

_____

What are some strategies you can use, when you feel yourself getting triggerd, to talk yourself off the ledge?

_____

_____

_____

If My Body Could Talk

1. Where in your body are you feeling something? If that part of you had a voice, what would it say to you? Speak fully and freely to yourself.

2. Reverse roles with that part of your body and write back to yourself. e.g. I am your gut and I am holding onto…

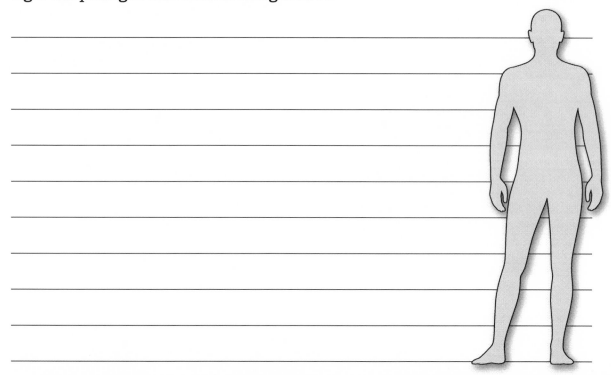

CHAPTER 4

Depression: Down the Rabbit Hole

Depression Self-Test

This questionnaire is designed to give you more information about the way that depression might be manifesting and affecting your life.

1. How much depression, do you feel?

   ○ *Almost none*   ○ *Very little*   ○ *Quite a bit*   ○ *Very much*

2. How much anxiety do you feel?

   ○ *Almost none*   ○ *Very little*   ○ *Quite a bit*   ○ *Very much*

3. How much emptiness do you feel?

   ○ *Almost none*   ○ *Very little*   ○ *Quite a bit*   ○ *Very much*

4. How much hopelessness/helplessness do you feel?

   ○ *Almost none*   ○ *Very little*   ○ *Quite a bit*   ○ *Very much*

5. How pessimistic or negative in your thinking are you?

   ○ *Almost none*   ○ *Very little*   ○ *Quite a bit*   ○ *Very much*

6. How much sadness do you feel?

   ○ *Almost none*   ○ *Very little*   ○ *Quite a bit*   ○ *Very much*

7. How much anger do you feel?

   ○ *Almost none*   ○ *Very little*   ○ *Quite a bit*   ○ *Very much*

8. How much sense of worthlessness do you feel?

   ○ *Almost none*   ○ *Very little*   ○ *Quite a bit*   ○ *Very much*

9. How much difficulty imagining a future do you have?

  ○ *Almost none*   ○ *Very little*   ○ *Quite a bit*   ○ *Very much*

10. How much fatigue or lethargy do you feel?

  ○ *Almost none*   ○ *Very little*   ○ *Quite a bit*   ○ *Very much*

11. How much is your sleep affected?

  ○ *Almost none*   ○ *Very little*   ○ *Quite a bit*   ○ *Very much*

12. How much is your weight affected?

  ○ *Almost none*   ○ *Very little*   ○ *Quite a bit*   ○ *Very much*

13. How irritable do you feel?

  ○ *Almost none*   ○ *Very little*   ○ *Quite a bit*   ○ *Very much*

14. How much trouble are you having concentrating?

  ○ *Almost none*   ○ *Very little*   ○ *Quite a bit*   ○ *Very much*

15. How much loss of interest in life, hobbies or sex do you feel?

  ○ *Almost none*   ○ *Very little*   ○ *Quite a bit*   ○ *Very much*

15. How much somatic disturbance, e.g. headaches, body aches, digestive disorders, chronic body pain that does not respond to treatment, do you feel?

  ○ *Almost none*   ○ *Very little*   ○ *Quite a bit*   ○ *Very much*

Depression Floor Check

| Depressed mood most days | | Diminished pleasure most days |

| Weight loss, weight gain | Sleeping Issues | Low energy, fatigue |

| Restlessness | | Irritability |

| Feelings of worthlessness | Anxiety | Helplessness/ collapse |

| Hopelessness | | Inappropriate guilt |

| Difficulty thinking, concentrating, making decisions | | Thoughts of death, suicidality |

| Other: |

Look over these manifestations of depression and answer the following questions:

Which manifestation pops out at you? Can you say something about that?

_____

_____

_____

If you experience depression, how does it manifest for you? What color is it?

_____

_____

_____

Did you grow up with or do live with anyone who is depressed?

_____

_____

_____

Do you think you carry someone else's depression or disappointment "for" them? If so say something about that.

_____

_____

_____

Do you have anger that you turn inwards, is there a part of you that you are angry with?

_____

_____

_____

If so, what does that part look like, what is their body position? Can you write a letter to that part of you?

_____

_____

_____

Dear _____,

_____

_____

_____

_____

_____

_____

_____

_____

_____

_____

_____

_____

_____

_____

❏ *From* ❏ *Warmly* ❏ *Every Yours* ❏ *Regards* ❏ *Lovingly*

Now can you reverse roles and write a letter back to your "adult self" *as* or *from* that part of yourself? What do you want your adult self to know about this part of yourself? Tell your adult self how you want your "inner adult" to manage you when you get low and have trouble asking for help.

Dear _____,

_____

_____

_____

_____

_____

_____

_____

_____

_____

_____

_____

_____

_____

_____

_____

_____

❏ *From*   ❏ *Warmly*   ❏ *Every Yours*   ❏ *Regards*   ❏ *Lovingly*

Exploring Your Dreams

Fill in the **ELEMENTS** of your dream in the empty circles below, fill in your name, and give your dream a title.

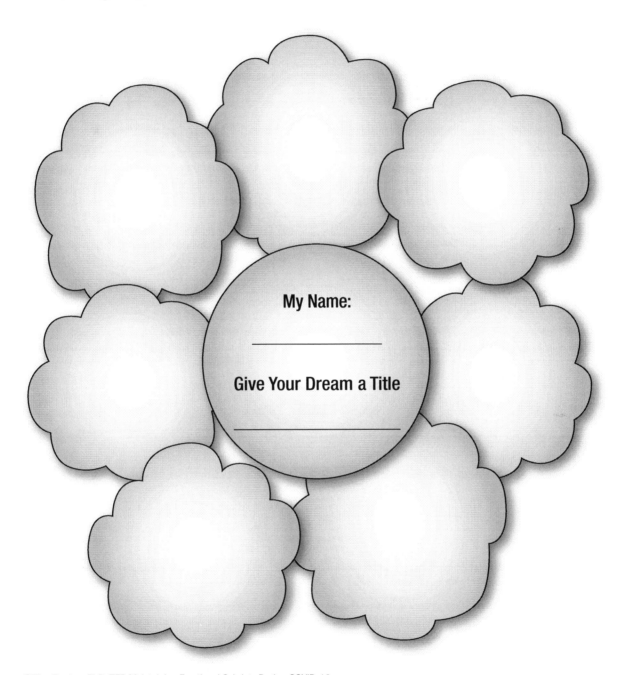

My Name:

_____

Give Your Dream a Title

_____

What do you notice as you look over the elements of your dream? Does anything jump out at you and if so what?

_____

_____

_____

What is your overall feeling as you look at your dream?

_____

_____

_____

Are there parts of your dream that surprise you? If so, why?

_____

_____

_____

Are there parts of your dream that make you uncomfortable? Can you describe the feeling?

_____

_____

_____

Are there parts of your dream that help you or give you courage?

_____

_____

_____

On the lines below, write the name of the part, element, person, place, thing, symbol, pet…(whatever is represented), then reverse roles with that part of you, and give yourself a personal message from that aspect of your dream back to your "real self".

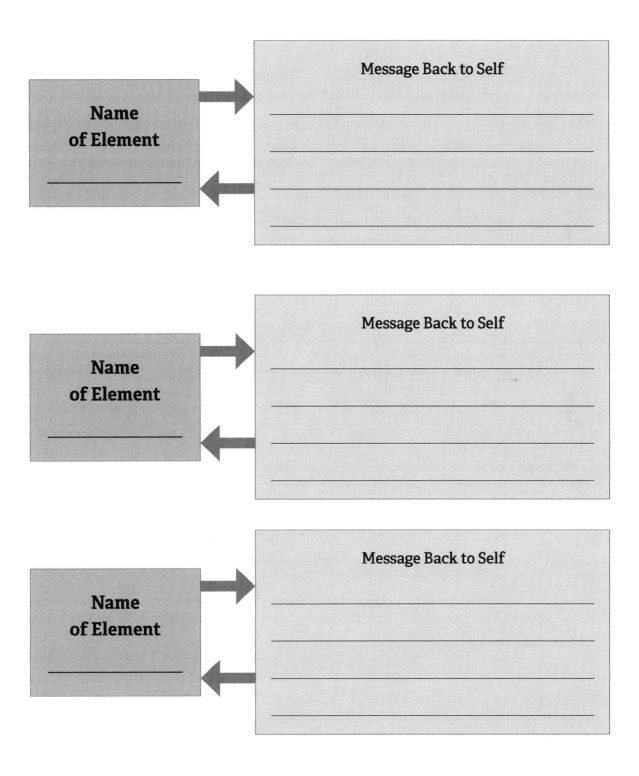

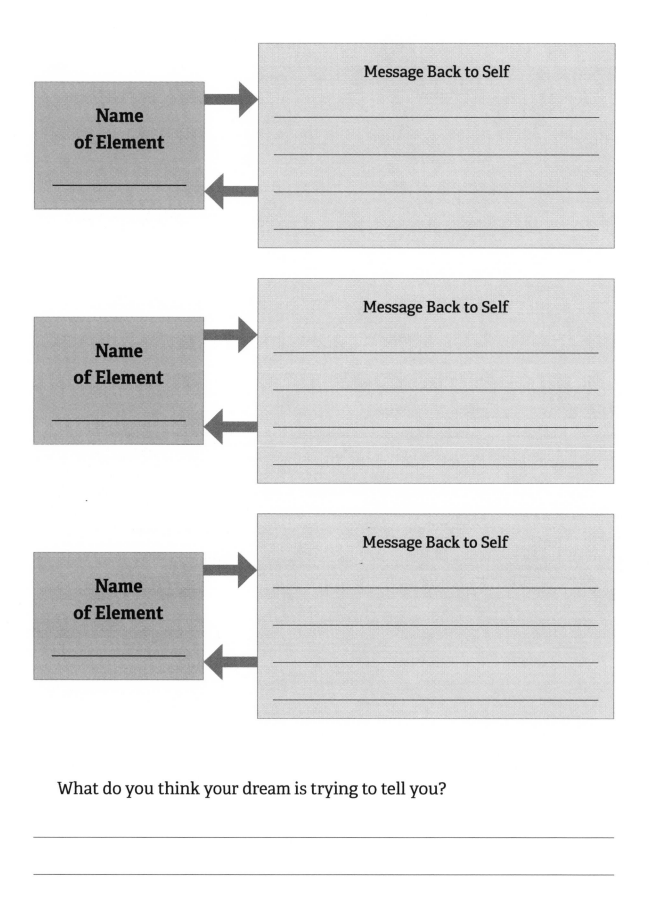

What do you think your dream is trying to tell you?

_____

_____

_____

CHAPTER 5

Self-Medicating: Numbing Out

Am I Self-Medicating My COVID-19 Related Feelings?

Answer the following questions by placing a check (✓) in the box that best describes "where you are."

1. How much emotional disregulation do you feel surrounding COVID-19?

   ○ *Almost none*   ○ *Very little*   ○ *Quite a bit*   ○ *Very much*

2. How blocked are you from getting in touch with your genuine feelings directly about or getting triggered by COVID-19?

   ○ *Almost none*   ○ *Very little*   ○ *Quite a bit*   ○ *Very much*

3. How disrupted in your daily routines do you feel?

   ○ *Almost none*   ○ *Very little*   ○ *Quite a bit*   ○ *Very much*

4. How much depression do you feel?

   ○ *Almost none*   ○ *Very little*   ○ *Quite a bit*   ○ *Very much*

5. How much helplessness/collapse do you feel?

   ○ *Almost none*   ○ *Very little*   ○ *Quite a bit*   ○ *Very much*

6. How numb or shut down are you?

   ○ *Almost none*   ○ *Very little*   ○ *Quite a bit*   ○ *Very much*

7. How much anger do you feel?

   ○ *Almost none*   ○ *Very little*   ○ *Quite a bit*   ○ *Very much*

8. How much pain from your past (historical pain) is getting triggered by COVID-19?

○ *Almost none*   ○ *Very little*   ○ *Quite a bit*   ○ *Very much*

9. How much fear of the future do you feel?

○ *Almost none*   ○ *Very little*   ○ *Quite a bit*   ○ *Very much*

10. How much anxiety/hypervigilance do you feel?

○ *Almost none*   ○ *Very little*   ○ *Quite a bit*   ○ *Very much*

11. How much COVID-19 related burnout are you experiencing?

○ *Almost none*   ○ *Very little*   ○ *Quite a bit*   ○ *Very much*

12. How willing are you to look at what might be getting triggered from your past that is affecting your ability to remain emotionally sober in your present, during COVID-19?

○ *Almost none*   ○ *Very little*   ○ *Quite a bit*   ○ *Very much*

13. How much is your body feeling for you (e.g. pain, soreness, breath-holding, lethargy, hyper-reactivity)?

○ *Almost none*   ○ *Very little*   ○ *Quite a bit*   ○ *Very much*

14. How disturbed is your sleep?

○ *Almost none*   ○ *Very little*   ○ *Quite a bit*   ○ *Very much*

15. How moody you feel?

○ *Almost none*   ○ *Very little*   ○ *Quite a bit*   ○ *Very much*

We're all feeling somewhat disoriented, we're wondering when this will end and how life will be "afterwards." We're uncertain. We feel trapped in a sort of limbo if not in our actual homes. Add to that historical pain that may get triggered, and you have a cocktail, a perfect storm, as it were, that can set you up to slip into moodiness, fear, irritability, and over-reaction. It can pile up and become bigger than it needs to be. It can lead to self-medication (reports already show that liquor sales are up). But using alcohol to manage your mood not only reduces your physical immunity (a known fact), it reduces your emotional immunity as well.

Drugs, alcohol, food, sex, and spending are temporary mood managers. They feel good in the moment, but they leave a trail of effects that can undermine your feeling of emotional fitness to meet the challenges of your day. You need extra rest, extra true calm, and extra self-discipline at a moment like this. Drinking to help you deal with being home with the kids will not help.

Seeing how grief might be manifesting for you, can be a first step in healing it. Unprocessed, hidden grief that is the result of previous trauma can wear many masks and can pop out when and where we least expect it. Some manifestations of unconscious grief can be:

- ✦ Sudden angry outbursts
- ✦ Rage
- ✦ Excessive rumination
- ✦ Chronic negativity
- ✦ Being easily triggered into overly intense emotional reactions or under-reactions/shutting down
- ✦ Recurring or long-lasting depression
- ✦ Chronic anxiety
- ✦ Self-mutilation and self-harming
- ✦ Caretaking behavior
- ✦ Excessive guilt

✦ Constant crying or feeling weepy

✦ Low mood, sad

✦ Excessive anxiety

✦ Emotional numbness or constriction

✦ Shame

✦ Codependency

✦ Body/health-related issues, soreness or stiffness

✦ A desire to self-medicate

The Wheel of Self-Medication

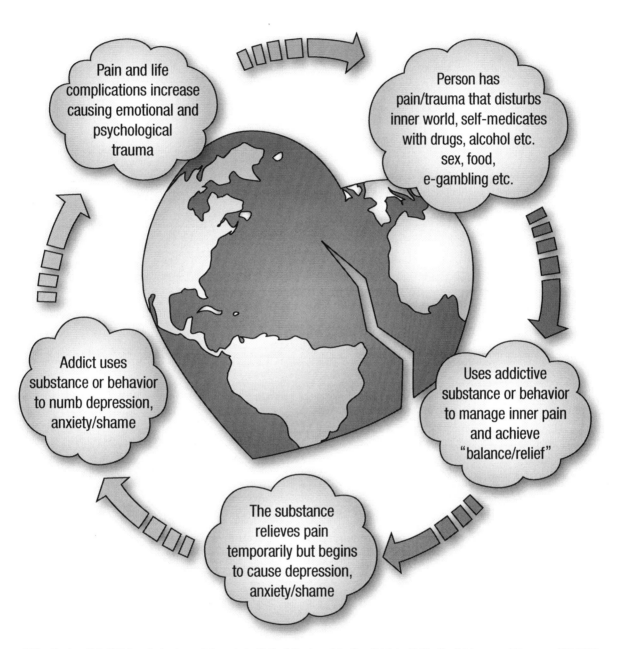

If you're doing some significant self-medication around COVID-19 itself or what it is triggering in you answer the following questions:

What is your "go to" for self-medication, especially during COVID-19?

_____

_____

_____

What does this give to you?

_____

_____

_____

What does this cost you? What does it take from you?

_____

_____

_____

How much trouble would you have modifying this behavior? Say a little about that, what would modification look like?

_____

_____

_____

How much trouble would you have giving this behavior up? Can you say why?

_____

_____

_____

CHAPTER 6
Hidden Grief

When Hidden Grief Gets Triggered During COVID-19 Confinement

If your feeling waves of sadness, anger, yearning or dislocation, "where has my life gone?" don't worry, it's normal. These are strange times and you are bound to feel that strangeness in a variety of ways. The idea is to feel these feelings and move through them so that you can get to the other side. Let them take their natural course, they won't last as long as you may think they will. Some sensations of depression can be caused by what we don't feel as much as what we do feel. When we foreclose on our inner world, our inner world starts to foreclose on us. We feel shut down inside. Processing/feeling emotion without acting out, going numb or self-medicating is healing. We bring split off parts of ourselves back into ourselves. And when you get to the other side, chances are you'll feel lighter and more integrated.

If There Is Hidden, Unprocessed Grief…

However, if you are getting stuck in emotions like depression, anxiety or chronic anger or rage, if you can't shake them, if they send you down a rabbit hole, you might be experiencing some old grief that is getting triggered by your current loss of "normal." Our sense of loss during the current COVID-19 crisis can trigger hidden emotions from when we experienced loss before. Whatever early losses you have had in your life—they are likely to have left an unconscious residue on your mind, an unseen wound that at moments like this can become sensitive under the pressure of the current crisis. Because of this sudden, frightening, and uncontrollable event that we're going through, we may re-experience when we felt blind-sided by life before, or when we felt helpless, trapped, scared, and unsafe. This can turn into a moment that throws you down a hole, or an opportunity to heal these sore spots, to take another look at them, feel them and understand their impact on your life and your inner world. Virtually anything that triggers the kind of old pain that we have pushed out of consciousness, or numbed can be a gift in disguise.

We refer to these types of ambiguous or unacknowledged, unrecognized losses as "disenfranchised losses." Disenfranchised losses that have remained hidden can get triggered and remerge without our knowing what is happening. The emotions that you experienced related to that earlier loss will very possibly reemerge at a moment like this, giving them the opportunity to be more fully felt, seen, accepted, understood, and, hence, further resolved.

Some examples of disenfranchised losses are:

- ✦ Loss of a connection to self, due to trauma

- ✦ The grief of the inner child who was neglected or outwardly abused by parents and now lives inside of the adult

- ✦ Divorce abandonment/visitation changes related to divorce

- ✦ Socially stigmatized deaths (AIDS, suicide, murder, DUI, overdose, death)

- ✦ Adoption either being adopted or placing a child up for adoption, or adoptive parents whose child seeks a biological family

- ✦ Death of a pet

- ✦ Miscarriage, infertility

- ✦ Disabling conditions, health issues

- ✦ Moving to a new home, job loss, retirement

- ✦ Mental illness or cognitive deficit

Disenfranchised grief (ambiguous): Some losses are hard to see and society doesn't recognize them and support us mourning them. And we ourselves may not be aware of the impact that these losses had on us, especially if we were very young or the pain was in some way denied. Divorce, abandonment, growing up with addiction, mental or physical illness, miscarriage, abortion, death of a pet, adoption, moving/loss of "home," job loss/retirement, or the loss of connection to a part of the self, due to trauma are all examples of this type of grief.

To Heal or Not to Heal:
Awakening vs. Reenacting Old Pain

Herein lies the challenge, when these tender places within us do get triggered, we tend to take one of two routes, the conscious route or the unconscious route.

The unconscious route: In the unconscious route, when these feelings reemerge and make us feel helpless and hopeless all over again, we do not make the connection between what might be getting triggered from our past into our present. So we act out or project our painful feelings from the past and make them about the people, places and things in our present. We dump them on everyone around us, making our current situation much more painful and volatile than it might otherwise be. Or we rage, we overeat or under-eat, act out sexually, spend, game, or engage in some other excessive behavior to go unconscious. Or we drink or drug, we self-medicate, we go numb. This is part of what's referred to as "masked grief," When someone is unable to identify that their symptoms or behaviors are connected to or related to some form of loss, they are masking their grief and it's emerging unconsciously.

The conscious route: In the conscious route, we use what is getting triggered as an opportunity to grow. When we do this, we can emerge stronger and more resilient, experiencing what psychologists call post-traumatic growth. We sit with the feelings and witness them in our mind's eye. And as we do this, we see what we normally do not see, the vulnerable and hurt part of ourselves that has stayed hidden comes before us, yearning for the comfort it did not get enough of. In the conscious route, we give comfort directly through accepting and loving this wounded part of ourselves. We become our own parent, our own best friend. We embrace and love rather than shut down, ignore, over-indulge, beat-up, or medicate. And by accepting what feels weak and needy within us, something paradoxical happens: We become less weak and needy, we become more whole.

Types of Grief Reactions

Normal grief tends to run its own course and lessen over time, although the time as well as the intensity may vary from person to person and also according to the timing, nature, and intensity of the loss itself. The following is an overview of the forms that more hidden, unconscious grief can take.

Anticipatory grief: With anticipatory grief, we feel grief in *anticipation of what could happen.* This is particularly relevant in this COVID-19 crisis because of our fear of becoming sick, the uncertainty about when life will return to normal, and what that normal might look like. We feel the loss of what was, of our normal routines, and we worry about what is to come.

Age correspondence reaction: For parents, when your child hits the age of a time in *your life when you were traumatized,* your unconscious pain from that time in your life may get triggered. If you do not make the connection between your past and your present (if you do not know it's old relational or situational pain getting triggered by a new relationship), you will tend to make your pain from the past about your present. You, the parent, may go to one extreme or the other. You may experience extra worry and anxiety for your child, you may want to over-protect your child because the child *in you* felt under-protected or unsafe. Or you may want to distance from your child, because the child in you wants to go numb, doesn't want to touch or feel that old wound.

Parental Inner Child Grief: I am naming and adding this catagory because I see so much of it in my practice. This happens to mothers and fathers who don't want to repeat the past but don't fully understand how to identify and validate the grief of the child who lives inside of them. They feel they are giving what they never got and when they give, they feel a kind of pain because the need in their child acts as a "reminder" or a trigger for the pain of their own, unmet childhood yearning and need. Parents need to attend to the wounds of their inner child so that they can gain some relief and healing, so that they can stop feeling like they are giving from and empty well.

Complicated grief: Complicated grief is the kind of grief that doesn't seem to resolve itself over time and becomes prolonged or chronic. This can occur due to the nature of the loss being sudden, violent, or hidden (e.g. prison or addiction), where we are ambivalent about the loss and don't really mourn it to begin with. Some warning signs of this kind of complex mourning could include self-medication, sexual acting out, self-harming behaviors, chronic and disabling feelings of guilt, worthlessness, suicidal thoughts, violence, or radical lifestyle changes. The age correspondence reaction may be seen as a form of complicated grief.

Inhibited grief: When a person does not let their grief show, whether it's because they want to keep it private or because they have hidden it even from themselves, their grief becomes inhibited. When someone cannot allow themselves to grieve, their body will do their crying for them. They may have physical symptoms like muscle stiffness, back pain, migraines, or illnesses that are directly connected to deep, emotional stress. Or they may act out or self-medicate.

Cumulative grief: Cumulative grief occurs when losses accumulate because they occur on top of each other. This may happen if the COVID-19 crisis continues to disrupt people's lives.

Collective grief: This a form of grief felt by a group. It might be racial, class-related, the death of a public figure, or the result of a natural disaster. Certainly, our world right now is experiencing a form of collective grief. It is important that we come together and "hold" each other through this time. The Italians singing out of their windows, the Greeks doing the Zorba dance on their rooftops, and the 12-Step community and other support communities moving online are all wonderful vehicles for sharing concerns so that the grief doesn't pile up get acted out in destructive ways. When we find the support we need to transform our grief into personal growth, we become more resilient.

Which form of grief are you experiencing right now. Write a few sentences describing how it feels for you... *Note:* You may be feeling several forms at once.

Normal grief : (Are you in touch with the loss of your day-to-day routines and connections or how COVID-19 has affected your life personally? What are you feeling?)

_____

_____

_____

_____

_____

_____

Anticipatory grief: (Are you feeling anxiety about what is to come?) What are you feeling?

_____

_____

_____

_____

_____

_____

Disenfranchised grief (ambiguous): (Do you have a pain residue from losses in your life that never got fully processed because they were not necessarily seen as important?) What losses? What are you feeling?

_____

_____

_____

_____

_____

_____

Age correspondence reaction: (is your child's stage of life, or way of being triggering something for you from that period in your life?) What are you feeling? (Are wounds from the past getting triggered into the present by your relationships? Or are you feeling trapped, unsafe, helpless, anxious or as if you're not going to be cared for?) Describe.

_____

_____

_____

_____

_____

_____

Inner Child Grief: Does your "inner child" need to mourn something, feeling unseen, unheard or neglected? Please describe.

_____

_____

_____

_____

_____

Complicated grief: (Do you have some hidden or un-looked at losses that you've never dealt with that complicate your ability to get close to others or or to manage your emotions during COVID-19?) What are you feeling?

_____

_____

_____

_____

Inhibited grief: (Do you have a hard time feeling your grief-related emotions?) What is in the way of your being able to feel your feelings?

_____

_____

_____

_____

_____

Cumulative grief: (Is COVID-19 just adding to a pile of other loss in your life?) If so, describe the legacy of losses.

_____

_____

_____

_____

_____

Collective grief: (Are you feeling grief for your world at this time?) What are you feeling?

_____

_____

_____

_____

_____

The Loss Chart

Directions: Losses can feel like they are piling up at moments like these. You may be experiencing more than one loss currently or feeling previous losses. Even losses from early childhood may be getting triggered by feeling trapped and helpless. In the center circle write the feeling of loss created by COVID-19 days. In the jutting lines write any other losses in your life that are getting triggered by your current feelings of loss.

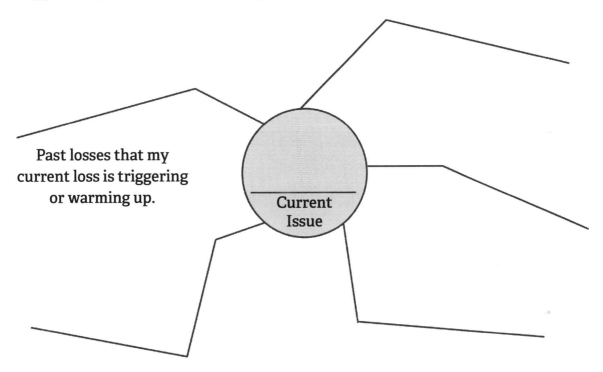

Past losses that my current loss is triggering or warming up.

Current Issue

©*Tian Dayton, PhD, TEP. Permission to reprint granted with the following attribution: Published in* The Soulful Journey of Recovery, *HCI, 2019.*

Write Letters as a way to work out more feelings…

Letter writing is an wonderful journaling technique that lets you talk to a person or a part of yourself. Letter-writing allows you to gain some distance and sense of space from the part of you that is struggling, it helps you to gain clarity and perspective, to remove the loss from being welded into your inner world and put it where you can see and communicate with it. These letters are not to be sent, they are for your eyes only! You can write any of the following letters or come up with your own letters. Once you have written them, you can either share them with a safe person (not the person you wrote them to) or your support group, do something symbolic like burn or bury the letter or simply do nothing with it if you feel finished. Here are a few possible letters you can write. Write a letter…

✦ To a part of yourself, the anxious part, the angry part, the resilient part or the depressed part. Once you have written a letter TO that part, reverse roles mentally and write a letter AS that part back to yourself. You might be surprised by what comes out! E.g, "As Dan's anger I want to tell you something and have you listen…" or, "I have been waiting much of my life for you to see me and accept me, for you to stop acting like I don't exist."

✦ Write a letter to someone to whom you have something you'd like to say.

✦ Write a letter to the "virus" or to "confinement" or to "COVID-19."

✦ Write a letter comforting and reassuring the part of yourself that is having trouble with confinement.

✦ Write a letter to the part of yourself that may be having trouble with self-care or care for others.

✦ Write a letter (again not to be sent) to anyone you're concerned about.

✦ Write a letter (again not to be sent) to anyone you're frustrated or angry with.

✦ Write a letter to your wounded inner child: Write a letter to your wounded, inner child in which you see their pain from feeling unheard, unseen, unvalued or in some way abused. Then reverse roles and write a letter back to your adult self from your inner child telling the adult part of you, how it feels to be seen and valued and thanking you for bringing them back into you in a more healed state. Thank the adult part of yourself and tell them all that you have to give to them and how exited you are to finally be able to give it.

✦ Write a letter to yourself as a child, a teenager or any age of your life that pulls you for some reason. Address anything that occurs to you from any stage. Then reverse roles and write a letter back to yourself from that part. Let that part of you speak freely and fully.

✦ Write a letter to the world!

Dear _____ ,

_____

_____

_____

_____

_____

_____

_____

_____

_____

_____

_____

_____

_____

_____

_____

_____

_____

_____

_____

_____

❑ *From*   ❑ *Warmly*   ❑ *Every Yours*   ❑ *Regards*   ❑ *Lovingly*

Dear _____,

_____

_____

_____

_____

_____

_____

_____

_____

_____

_____

_____

_____

_____

_____

_____

_____

_____

_____

_____

_____

_____

❑ *From*　❑ *Warmly*　❑ *Every Yours*　❑ *Regards*　❑ *Lovingly*

CHAPTER 7
From Trauma to Emotional Sobriety

Trauma and Emotional
Sobriety Self-Test

This is a self-test designed to increase both the impact trauma has had on you and your awareness about your own level of emotional sobriety.

1. Do you feel emotionally numb or out of touch with your emotions in certain areas of your life?

   ○ *Almost none*   ○ *Very little*   ○ *Quite a bit*   ○ *Very much*

2. Do you have bouts of depression and despair that do not resolve themselves in a reasonable amount of time?

   ○ *Almost none*   ○ *Very little*   ○ *Quite a bit*   ○ *Very much*

3. Are you constantly waiting for the bottom to fall out; do you mistrust calm and orderly living?

   ○ *Almost none*   ○ *Very little*   ○ *Quite a bit*   ○ *Very much*

4. Do you tend to go from 0–10 in your emotional life and have trouble staying on middle ground do you have trouble regulating your intense emotions?

   ○ *Almost none*   ○ *Very little*   ○ *Quite a bit*   ○ *Very much*

5. Do you feel you recreate the same problems over and over again getting stuck in the same place?

   ○ *Almost none*   ○ *Very little*   ○ *Quite a bit*   ○ *Very much*

6. Do you have trouble identifying what you really feel?

   ○ *Almost none*   ○ *Very little*   ○ *Quite a bit*   ○ *Very much*

7. Do your feelings evidence themselves as body sensations such as headaches, stomachaches, backaches, instead of as conscious feelings?

   ○ *Almost none*   ○ *Very little*   ○ *Quite a bit*   ○ *Very much*

8. Do you have larger-than-appropriate emotional reactions when some sort of situation or interaction triggers you?

   ○ *Almost none*   ○ *Very little*   ○ *Quite a bit*   ○ *Very much*

9. Do you have trouble taking in help and support from others?

   ○ *Almost none*   ○ *Very little*   ○ *Quite a bit*   ○ *Very much*

10. Do you isolate and have trouble being in community or intimate relationships?

   ○ *Almost none*   ○ *Very little*   ○ *Quite a bit*   ○ *Very much*

11. Do you feel guilty when your life improves?

   ○ *Almost none*   ○ *Very little*   ○ *Quite a bit*   ○ *Very much*

12. Do you self-medicate your feelings or try to alter your mood with drugs?

   ○ *Almost none*   ○ *Very little*   ○ *Quite a bit*   ○ *Very much*

13. Do you engage in high-risk behaviors in order to "feel alive"?

   ○ *Almost none*   ○ *Very little*   ○ *Quite a bit*   ○ *Very much*

14. Do you experience more anxiety than you feel is normal?

   ○ *Almost none*   ○ *Very little*   ○ *Quite a bit*   ○ *Very much*

15. Do you find yourself avoiding situations that are reminiscent of previous painful situations?

   ○ *Almost none*   ○ *Very little*   ○ *Quite a bit*   ○ *Very much*

16. Do you have a hard time envisioning your future?

◯ *Almost none*   ◯ *Very little*   ◯ *Quite a bit*   ◯ *Very much*

17. Do you experience flashbacks or nightmares that are reminiscent of your trauma or are otherwise upsetting?

◯ *Almost none*   ◯ *Very little*   ◯ *Quite a bit*   ◯ *Very much*

18. Do you experience intrusive thoughts related to your trauma(s)?

◯ *Almost none*   ◯ *Very little*   ◯ *Quite a bit*   ◯ *Very much*

One of the tragedies of trauma, if we don't go through the necessary grief process to wake up our inner world and feel what we could not feel at the time, is that we lose chunks of our own, personal history. Grief is what gives these disowned parts of ourselves, back to us. We feel what we could not feel and as we do, we begin to understand ourselves. We fit the disparate, shattered pieces of self, back into the full mosaic of our lives. And trauma can keep us from remembering not only what felt bad, but also what felt good. So in grieving our traumatized parts of self, we also have a chance to reclaim our joy.

From Trauma to Emotional Sobriety

Trauma shuts our inner world down. Feeling is the bridge towards emotional literacy. We have to first be able to feel our feelings with enough safety so that we can find the words to identify and describe them to ourselves and others. Notice I only said *enough* safety, because it rarely feels entirely safe to feel these exiled emotions, this exiled self, who for protection went underground. Through this process we learn emotional literacy. There is great freedom and mastery in this. And this kind of emotional literacy opens the door to our being able to resolve old, painfilled, frozen and semi-conscious material by feeling it, finding words and allowing a new narrative of events to organically take shape within us.

Not everyone responds to trauma in the same way. The complicating factor it not only what happens to us on the outside but how we experience it on the inside. Some people, because of risk factors either from childhood or the ways in which they handle emotions, may experience trauma more intensely than others. What are our pre-trauma risk factors? How do they impact how we experience trauma? What are the buffering elements that do or do not exist in our lives that will ameliorate the way we're experiencing unusual stress like reliable relationships, comfortable living situations, jobs, money, food or support communities? And what attitudes are we able to summon that might help us to make a bad situation better?

What Do We Mean
by Pre-trauma Risk Factors?

Pre trauma risk factors are personality traits, family or social conditions and/or high-risk behaviors that can put one in a higher risk category for developing PTSD.

According to the PTSD Alliance the following are pre-trauma risk factors that can make one more likely to develop PTSD, "the level of severe trauma experienced during and since early childhood. Family instability, lack of a social support system, or poverty. Women are twice as likely to develop PTSD than men. Having a pre-existing emotional or mental health disorder, eating disorder, or drug/alcohol abuse."

Some common pre-trauma risk factors are:

+ **Previous exposure to trauma:** What is your trauma history? Did you grow up with adverse childhood experiences or traumatic experiences in which you experienced helplessness and horror. (Life Events Checklist (LEC; Gray *et al.* 2004).

+ **Coping Styles:** How have you learned to adapt to traumatic experiences in the past and how did you see those who raised you adapt, what did you see modeled?

+ **Emotional or Mental Health Issues:** What is your previous history of mental health problems that might influence how you experience this current crisis. (Structured Clinical Interview for the Diagnostic and Statistical Manual of Mental Disorders, fourth edition (DSM-IV) (SCID; First *et al.* 1996)

+ **Alcohol consumption or other forms of addiction:** Are you self-medicating to manage your uncomfortable feelings and to what extent? What is your level of alcohol use that will make you less able to cope effectively with this current crisis. (Liu, Tarigan, Bromet, & Kim, 2014) (Pietrzak *et al.,* 2014). Other forms of addiction also have an effect here such as drug use, vaping or process addictions such as gaming/internet, sexual acting out etc. and eating disorders.

✦ **Dissociative experiences:** Do you remain present in the moment? Or do you experience depersonalization and derealization or feeling disconnected from your thoughts, feelings, memories, and surroundings.

✦ **Anxiety sensitivity:** How fearful are you to specific anxiety-related thoughts, feelings and sensations and to what extent do you believe these sensations to have catastrophic consequences.

✦ **Attitudes around expressing emotion:** How comfortable are you sharing what you feel so that it doesn't build up and turn into anxiety, depression or self-medication, so that you don't implode or explode? What's your ability to Share Feelings vs reluctance to talk about negative feelings or problems. The Attitudes to Emotional Expression questionnaire (Williams *et al.* 1995) assesses negative attitudes towards talking about feelings.

✦ **Depressive attributions:** What is your internal dialogue or monologue? Do you engage in negative thinking, negative projections, negative ruminations or dark narratives that can contribute to depression and generally undermine your sense of wellbeing? (The Depressive Attributions Questionnaire (Kleim *et al.* 2011)

✦ **Social support:** How well do you access and utilize the supports that are available to you and seek out support from family, friends and community resources.

✦ **Resilience to stress:** Can you see stress as a challenge that you will meet and grow through and set about mobilizing the kinds of supports that will help you do this? What's the extent to which you experience aspects of resilience such as confidence in your ability to deal with challenges and problems. The Connor–Davidson Resilience Questionnaire (CD-RISC; Connor & Davidson, 2003)

We can learn to trade non helpful responses to memories of stressful events such as suppression, rumination, intentional numbing. isolation, wishful thinking/denial or self-medication for more helpful coping styles such as those explored throughout this workbook. And we can adopt some of the protective measures that we discussed in the introduction and we can consciously build resources into our lives to buffer stress and strengthen our ability to meet challenges more successfully.

The Trauma Timeline

Jot down whatever incidents or relational dynamics from your own life, that felt highly stressful, painful or traumatizing to you.

_____   80 years   _____

_____   75 years   _____

_____   70 years   _____

_____   65 years   _____

_____   60 years   _____

_____   55 years   _____

_____   50 years   _____

_____   45 years   _____

_____   40 years   _____

_____   35 years   _____

_____   30 years   _____

_____   25 years   _____

_____   20 years   _____

_____   15 years   _____

_____   10 years   _____

_____   5 years   _____

_____   0 years   _____

Look over your Trauma Time Line and answer the following questions:

How do you feel when you look over your entire time line?

_____

_____

_____

_____

_____

What jumps out at you about it, what do you notice in particular?

_____

_____

_____

_____

_____

Were there times in your life when traumas seemed to cluster together or overlap in some way?

_____

_____

_____

_____

_____

Were there times in your life that seem relatively free of trauma? Did this surprise you in any way?

_____

_____

_____

_____

_____

Did the trauma related feelings and thinking stop when the traumas stopped or did they persist in some way, did they still affect you and undermine your emotional sobriety? Are they affecting you today in this COVID-19 period? If so, how are they manifesting?

_____

_____

_____

_____

_____

_____

_____

_____

_____

_____

When you look at your Trauma Time Line do you see repeating patterns? If so describe how and with whom they play out. e.g. "When my son is defiant I treat him the way my father treated me even though I know it hurt me."

_____

_____

_____

_____

_____

_____

Do you have anything you'd like to say to yourself at some point along your timeline, from yourself today? e.g. Dear 4th grade self, I want you to know that I see your struggle trying to please or fit in with _____ and it won't last forever." etc.

_____

_____

_____

_____

_____

_____

Give your younger self a sneak preview, tell them how what they are going through will serve them later, how it will make them more resilient!

_____

_____

_____

_____

_____

A Letter of Forgiveness to Someone

If you feel like if, write a letter to someone you'd like to feel forgiveness towards (for your own healing, not to be sent) telling them how they hurt you, how angry you have been, what it cost you and why you want to let them go and move on, for your own sake.

Dear _____ ,

_____

_____

_____

_____

_____

_____

_____

_____

_____

_____

_____

_____

_____

_____

_____

❑ *From*   ❑ *Warmly*   ❑ *Every Yours*   ❑ *Regards*   ❑ *Lovingly*

A Letter Forgiving Yourself

Write a letter to yourself, as a child, a teenager an adult or all of these on separate sheets of paper, forgiving yourself for being so young, hurting, vulnerable and taken advantage of. Forgive yourself fully, freely and with love. Hold this part of yourself safe inside of you.

Dear _____ ,

_____

_____

_____

_____

_____

_____

_____

_____

_____

_____

_____

_____

❑ *From*   ❑ *Warmly*   ❑ *Every Yours*   ❑ *Regards*   ❑ *Lovingly*

Role Reversal Forgiveness

Now reverse roles and write a letter back to yourself from this part of you. Forgive your adult self for not seeing and accepting this part of you or for acting out pain instead of feeling it. For ignoring, rejecting or even hating this part of you and express your pleasure at being seen, held and loved by your adult self.

Dear _____,

_____

_____

_____

_____

_____

_____

_____

_____

_____

_____

_____

_____

_____

❏ *From*   ❏ *Warmly*   ❏ *Every Yours*   ❏ *Regards*   ❏ *Lovingly*

CHAPTER 8
Resilience: Owning My Strengths

Resilience

Research on resilience finds that those who thrive in situations that might defeat others, have somehow figured out how to mobilize their supports and make use of them. They have a sense of reality and acceptance about their circumstances but they are proactive in taking steps to make things better. A resilient person tends to be able to lean into supports that allow them to make the best of a situation."Resilience depends on supportive, responsive relationships and mastering a set of capabilities that can help us respond and adapt to adversity in healthy ways," says Jack Shonkoff, MD, director of the Center on the Developing Child at Harvard. "It's those capacities and relationships that can turn toxic stress into tolerable stress."

Here are some of the basic factors that appear over and over again as common threads when it comes to understanding what goes into creating resilience. Resilient kids tend to have:

✦ The availability of at least one stable, caring, and supportive relationship between a child and an adult caregiver.

✦ A sense of mastery over life circumstances.

✦ Strong executive function and self-regulation skills.

✦ The supportive context of affirming faith or cultural traditions. (Walsh, 2015)

Wong and Wong, two researchers on resilience propose that certain qualities of behavioral resilience can only be developed from actual experience of having overcome adversities (Wong and Wong, 2012). These researchers identified at least three typical patterns that resilient people appear to display that I think are useful to know. They see these qualities as being developed through facing and meeting life's challenges; they are dynamic, constantly evolving qualities rather than qualities residing only within the individual.

1. **Recovery:** bouncing back and returning to normal functioning.

2. **Invulnerability:** remaining relatively unscathed by the adversity or trauma in their lives in terms of their ability to function well.

3. **Post-traumatic growth:** bouncing back and becoming stronger, learning and growing through adversity. (Wong & Wong, 2012).

In other research on children from families affected by violence, poverty, substance abuse, racism, or family disruption, Sybil and Steven Wolin found that one of the qualities that resilient people often possessed was "survivor's pride" or a feeling of having met their challenges and prevailed. One can hear this in soldiers who have faced life-and- death situations and survived or those who have survived traumatizing situations and thrived even against the odds or in spite of, or even because of adversity. Sybil and Steven Wolin (1994) identified seven qualities that resilient people possessed, that helped them to thrive where others did not.

+ *Insight.* This is the ability to see people and situations in some degree of depth. They are able to see into a situation, they are perceptive and can benefit from their discerning awareness.

+ *Independence.* Resilient kids and adults, Wolin and Wolin found, had a natural or perhaps a developed independence; they could think for themselves, act autonomously, and also create space between themselves and their troubles or difficult situations or families.

+ *Relationships.* Resilient people were able to have and enjoy relationships and to feel sustained, supported, and nourished by them. They could give as well as accept caring from others.

+ *Initiative.* This refers to the ability to take initiative on one's own or another's behalf, to take action to make a situation better, and to hang in there and show perseverance and doggedness.

+ *Creativity.* Resilient kids and adults can come up with creative solutions to complex problems; they can think outside of the box.

They often have their own creative sides and can take pleasure and pride from their own creative endeavors or appreciate and enjoy those of others.

✦ *Humor.* Resilient people keep their sense of humor; they are able to turn a tough situation on its head and have a laugh at it.

✦ *Morality.* Resilient people tend to have a moral code that they live by, one from which they can draw strength and a sense of direction. It can relate to spirituality, to nature, to the universe, or to living a good and decent life for one's self and others. Dayton (2019)

Resilience Floor Check

Problem Solving Skills

Sensitivity

Ability to Reach Out

Humility

Spiritual Change

Stick-to-itiveness

Inventiveness

Humor

A Desire Not to Self-Medicate

Appreciation of Life

Inner Strength/Self Reliance

Increased Appreciation of Life

Can Do Attitude/Optimism

A Sense of Mastery

Relationships/Better Relating to Others

Courage

Willingness to Change

Creativity

Willingness to Fail and Try Again

Empathy

Dedication to Healthy Self Care

Clear Thinking

New Possibilities/An Attitude that Life Will Work Out

Knowing How to Feel Good and Have Fun

Life Balance

Other

Glance over these qualities. Which one pops out at you and why do you think it feels meaningful to you at this point in time?

_____

_____

_____

_____

Next, which one (s) do you think you developed through meeting and dealing with challenging circumstances in your life? How do you feel about yourself having done this?

_____

_____

_____

_____

Which of these qualities do you feel you modeled from someone significant in your life and who is the person who had it? What would you like to say to that person about how they impacted you?

_____

_____

_____

_____

Which quality (s) do you feel others value in you? Why do you feel they value it/them?

_____

_____

_____

_____

_____

Which quality(s) does someone close to you have that you chose to bring into your life through this relationship? State the relationship and the quality and a sentence about why it's important to you.

_____

_____

_____

_____

_____

Which quality(s) do you feel you're in the process of developing? And/or which qualities or behaviors are you mobilizing most to deal with COVID-19?

_____

_____

_____

_____

_____

The Mask Monologue

"Walking in the street with a mask is an emotional experience, and we can validly use this experience as a moment of emotional self-reflection and emotional integration/regulation" says Christophe Sauerwein, MBA, MSc, in this exercise he has suggested. "It is a salient occasion to constructively exercise our emotional dash-board." We ask ourselves,

- ✦ Do I feel, safe?

- ✦ What do I notice as I breathe in and out (through the mask, which is different than normal)?

- ✦ Does wearing a mask dictate my physical boundaries with others?

- ✦ What sort of message do I send out to others?

- ✦ How do I imagine I am perceived by others?

- ✦ How do I experience myself and feel about giving this message to others?

- ✦ How do I experience and feel about others wearing (or not wearing) a mask?

On the following lines, write a monologue examining these questions in the first person: e.g. Wearing this mask I feel…etc.

_____

_____

_____

_____

_____

_____

_____

And the ultimate test: Now imagine removing the mask, how does it feel?

What did you learn about yourself from writing this?

What masks might you be wearing in your own life?

How do you experience yourself "beneath the mask"?

And now, how do you experience yourself when you imagine taking the mask off?

CHAPTER 9
Gratitude and Post-Traumatic Growth

Post-Traumatic Growth Inventory

Clients Name: _____   Today's Date: _____

Indicate for each of the statements below the degree to which this change occurred in your life as a result of the crisis/disaster, using the following scale.

0 = I did not experience this change as a result of my crisis.

1 = I experienced this change to a very small degree as a result of my crisis.

2 = I experienced this change to a small degree as a result of my crisis.

3 = I experienced this change to a moderate degree as a result of my crisis.

4 = I experienced this change to a great degree as a result of my crisis.

5 = I experienced this change to a very great degree as a result of my crisis.

Possible Areas of Growth and Change	0	1	2	3	4	5
1. I changed my priorities about what is important in life.	○	○	○	○	○	○
2. I have a greater appreciation for the value of my own life.	○	○	○	○	○	○
3. I devloped new interests.	○	○	○	○	○	○
4. I have a greater feeling of self-reliance.	○	○	○	○	○	○
5. I have a better understanding of spiritual matters.	○	○	○	○	○	○
6. I more clearly see that I can count on people in times of trouble.	○	○	○	○	○	○
7. I established a new path for my life.	○	○	○	○	○	○
8. I have a greater sense of closeness with others.	○	○	○	○	○	○

9. I am more willing to express my emotions.   ○ ○ ○ ○ ○ ○

10. I know better that I can handle difficulties.   ○ ○ ○ ○ ○ ○

11. I am able to do better things with my life.   ○ ○ ○ ○ ○ ○

12. I am better able to accept the way things work out.   ○ ○ ○ ○ ○ ○

13. I can better appreciate each day.   ○ ○ ○ ○ ○ ○

14. New opportunities are available which wouldn't have been otherwise.   ○ ○ ○ ○ ○ ○

15. I have more compassion for others.   ○ ○ ○ ○ ○ ○

16. I put more effort into my relationships.   ○ ○ ○ ○ ○ ○

17. I am more likely to try to change things which need changing.   ○ ○ ○ ○ ○ ○

18. I have a stronger religious faith.   ○ ○ ○ ○ ○ ○

19. I discovered that I'm stronger than I thought I was.   ○ ○ ○ ○ ○ ○

20. I learned a great deal about how wonderful people are.   ○ ○ ○ ○ ○ ○

21. I better accept needing others.   ○ ○ ○ ○ ○ ○

Post-Traumatic Growth

One of the conundrums of therapy is that it often gives the impression that expressing feelings will automatically lead to their resolution. And when I say that you need to feel repressed or dissociated emotions in order to heal them, I realize that I seem to be reinforcing that. But there is a fine line between knowing and expressing them and being stuck in and constantly recycling and re-litigating them. The reason we need to feel those emotions that we've blocked out, is so that we can translate them into words and hold them out in the light of our own mind and our relationships so that we can use this beautiful prefrontal cortex, this thinking mind, as the incisive tool that it is—an instrument of logic and understanding. Then we can bring those parts of ourselves that are numb back into a state of sentience and aliveness. We can self-reflect, understand, develop empathy both for ourselves and others and move on. *(Dayton, 2019)*

One of the ways that we heal from trauma is by seeing and making meaning and purpose out of challenging circumstances. Making positive meaning and creating a positive narrative that includes a broader more compassionate world view, lights a path towards happy relationships and inner growth.

Some people create meaning and purpose by demonizing another person, sect, race or country. The meaning that they make in some way pathologies the other guy whether the other guy is our parents, political figures, another race or religion or country. When we do this, we point the finger of blame at each other, we pass the hot potato from person to person and everyone does what they can to avoid it landing on their laps. This is pathology-making, because the behaviors we adopt are defensive in nature and get us stuck in defensive/aggressive positions.

The Post-Traumatic Growth Timeline can help you to see how you grew from trauma, at what points in your life a door flew open and you saw a new way and followed it. Understanding where you made positive choices and benefited from them and built on them becomes something you can internalize and own.

We can do a timeline that includes a period before the COVID-19 days and it can even go beyond them. We can reflect on what we thought of life before and how these days may be changing our world view or our more intimate view of ourselves and our relationships. We can also walk into our future a bit and enter ways in which we might fear what is coming or deal with challenges to come, who we might become. We can talk "to" ourselves anywhere along this timeline either through role play, dialogging or writing letters to ourselves in the past, present and future. After we have completed the timeline we can share about what came up and what growth in ourselves we became aware of.

Pre-COVID-19 Life

Write whatever time period you're looking at, inside of the circles.

In the lines to the left, write what you were doing during these months. On the lines to the right, write how you were feeling.

During COVID-19 Life

Write whatever time period you're looking at, inside of the circles.

In the lines to the left, write what you were/are doing during these months.

On the lines to the right, write how you were/are feeling.

Post-COVID-19 Life

In the lines to the left, write a "future projection" scene or what you hope, imagine or fear you will be doing during those months. On the lines to the right, write how you imagine you will be feeling when you're doing what you long to do, (a positive projection) or what you fear, (a fearful or negative projection) you might be doing or simply what you imagine or predict you might do, (a future projection).

#1 _____   (A FEARED DARK SCENE)   _____

_____   _____

_____   _____

_____   ( )   _____

_____   _____

#2 _____   _____

_____   (A REALISTIC SCENE)   _____

_____   _____

_____   _____

#3 _____   ( )   _____

_____   _____

_____   (A "WISHED FOR" SCENE)   _____

_____   _____

How Gratitude Changes You and Your Brain

Research by Joel Wong and Joshua Brown of Indiana University used neuro-imaging to see how the brain reacted to gratitude. "Most interestingly, when we compared those who wrote the gratitude letters with those who didn't, the gratitude letter writers showed greater activation in the medial prefrontal cortex when they experienced gratitude in the MRI scanner. This is striking as this effect was found three months after the letter writing began. This indicates that simply expressing gratitude may have lasting effects on the brain."

Activities like keeping a gratitude list, expressing gratitude either in words or letter form seems to make positive emotions "sticky" which in my opinion can help to counter the phenomenon that I see so often as a psychologist of how "sticky" negative thinking can be. Wong and Brown report that, "compared with the participants who wrote about negative experiences or only received counseling, those who wrote gratitude letters reported significantly better mental health four weeks and 12 weeks after their writing exercise ended. This suggests that gratitude writing can be beneficial not just for healthy, well-adjusted individuals, but also for those who struggle with mental health concerns. In fact, it seems, practicing gratitude on top of receiving psychological counseling carries greater benefits than counseling alone, even when that gratitude practice is brief." Following are some of the gratitude "interventions" that research finds help mood and mental health:

Write a thank-you letter. Write a letter to someone who has made a difference in your life and express your gratitude for what they did for you.

Thank someone mentally. If writing isn't your thing just think about someone who has done something nice for you, and mentally thank them for it.

Pray and count your blessings. People who are inclined can use prayer to cultivate gratitude alongside the practice of counting blessings which is another form of a gratitude list of giving "thanks."

Reflect: Nothing fancy here. Just think about what you're grateful for as you sip your tea of coffee. Cozy up and meditate on what is fine in life, what you feel grateful for and blessed to have in your life. Be mindful and appreciate what you have.

Keep a gratitude list: The twelve-step community has made this a core practice for many, many years. It helps to maintain "an attitude of gratitude" to actually increase the blessings in your life by appreciating what you already have and to keep you emotionally sober.

Relapse tends to happen emotionally, psychologically, behaviorally and spiritually, before the relapse into poorer mental health, process additions, drugs or alcohol occurs. And this is equally true for adult children of addicts or codependents as it is for those who abuse substances. It happens on the inside before it happens on the outside. Gratitude is a counter weight to what the twelve-step world has long referred to as "stinkin-thinkin." Gratitude is active, it pulls us out of collapse and toward conscious awareness. It brings us towards emotional sobriety.

The Gratitude List and Letter

Current research by the Positive Psychology field has underscored the life-enhancing effect of gratitude. The Gratitude Letter is at the top of their list for mood benefits that last up to a month.

Two psychologists, Dr. Robert A. Emmons of the University of California, Davis, and Dr. Michael E. McCullough of the University of Miami, have done much of the research on gratitude. In one study, they asked all participants to write a few sentences each week, focusing on particular topics.

One group wrote about things they were grateful for that had occurred during the week. A second group wrote about daily irritations or things that had displeased them, and the third wrote about events that had affected them (with no emphasis on them being positive or negative). After 10 weeks, those who wrote about gratitude were more optimistic and felt better about their lives. They also exercised more and had fewer visits to physicians than those who focused on sources of aggravation.

Another leading researcher in this field, Dr. Martin E. P. Seligman, a psychologist at the University of Pennsylvania, tested the impact of various positive psychology interventions on 411 people, each compared with a control assignment of writing about early memories. When their week's assignment was to write and personally deliver a letter of gratitude to someone who had never been properly thanked for his or her kindness, participants immediately exhibited a huge increase in happiness scores. This impact was greater than that from any other intervention, with benefits lasting for a month.

Of course, studies such as this one cannot prove cause and effect. But most of the studies published on this topic support an association between gratitude and an individual's well-being.

Other studies have looked at how gratitude can improve relationships. For example, a study of couples found that individuals who took time to express gratitude for their partner not only felt more positive toward the other person but also felt more comfortable expressing concerns about their relationship.

Gratitude Letter

Write a letter thanking someone for what they did for you and describing the impact they had on your life.

Dear _____ ,

_____

_____

_____

_____

_____

_____

_____

_____

_____

_____

_____

_____

_____

_____

_____

❏ *From*   ❏ *Warmly*   ❏ *Every Yours*   ❏ *Regards*   ❏ *Lovingly*

Gratitude List

1. _____

_____

_____

2. _____

_____

_____

3. _____

_____

_____

4. _____

_____

_____

5. _____

_____

_____

6. _____

_____

_____

Write a Letter to Yourself telling yourself what positive changes you see in yourself, and thanking yourself for all that you have given to yourself and those around you as a result of your hard work and perseverance.

Dear _____,

_____

_____

_____

_____

_____

_____

_____

_____

_____

_____

_____

_____

_____

_____

_____

_____

_____

❏ *From*   ❏ *Warmly*   ❏ *Every Yours*   ❏ *Regards*   ❏ *Lovingly*

A Letter to Myself in the Future

Write a letter to yourself at some point in the future after the threat of COVID-19 has passed, reminding yourself of what you are learning now through this experience that you don't want to forget or lose—the lessons or learnings that you'd like to hang onto.

Dear _____ ,

_____

_____

_____

_____

_____

_____

_____

_____

_____

_____

_____

_____

_____

_____

_____

❏ *From*   ❏ *Warmly*   ❏ *Every Yours*   ❏ *Regards*   ❏ *Lovingly*

CHAPTER 10
Learning to Self-Soothe

Guided Meditations and Imageries

Meditations and guided imageries teach the skills of mindfulness while giving you a full out "spa break"!

Guided relaxations help to balance the nervous system and teach the skills of self-regulation, deep breathing and relaxation. They also provide opportunities for skill building in processing emotions which can help in regulating behaviors. Emotions have a motor aspect and tend to lead towards some form of action—in other words, they make us want to do something. Guided imagery allows us to learn how to become conscious of our own emotional and mental processes. Athletes use guided imagery to improve their athletic performance. The act of picturing a perfect run down a mountain or catching a ball, for example, can serve as mental practice that the body is actually able to translate into action. Picturing our day going well or being able to do a task in a relaxed manner rather than a stressed-out way follows the same formula. Guided relaxations, meditations and imageries can help us to manage our COVID-19 days more successfully. If you log onto *tiandayton.com/COVID-19 resources*, I have free guided imageries for deep relaxation, cultivating calm and processing grief and anger as well as others. I even have one for kids to teach breathing, relaxation and self-regulation.

The Physical Benefits of Guided Meditation and Imagery

Clinical research has demonstrated that guided imagery can reduce preoperative anxiety and post- operative pain among patients undergoing cardiac surgery. In 1998, the cardiac surgery team at Inova Heart Center, Inova Fairfax Hospital, 3300 Gallows Road, Falls Church, VA led by Halpin LS, Speir AM, Capo Bianco P. Barnett SD, broke up pre- and post-surgery patients into two groups: one that used guided imagery and one that did not use guided imagery. Data was collected relative to both patient satisfaction and hospital costs. The data showed that patients who completed the guided imagery program had a shorter average length of stay, a decrease in average direct pharmacy costs, and a decrease in average direct pain medication costs while maintaining high overall patient satisfaction with the care and treatment provided. Not surprisingly, guided imagery is now considered a complementary medical means to reduce anxiety, pain, and length of stay among this and many hospital's cardiac surgery patients. (Dayton, 2020)

Self-Soothing and Self-Regulation

Most of us don't realize that self-hypnosis is a natural state; it is an altered state that we move in and out of throughout the day, like when we go into a trance driving along a highway or watching TV. "Self-hypnosis taps into a natural 'basal ganglia' soothing power source that most people do not even know exists," says Daniel G. Amen. "It is found within you, within your ability to focus your concentration. The basal ganglia region of the brain is involved with integrating feelings and movement, shifting and smoothing motor behavior, setting the body's idle speed or anxiety level, modulating motivation, and driving feelings of pleasure and ecstasy."

Trauma can cause us to become deregulated in the basal ganglia region. The basal ganglia can become reset to be constantly on the alert or hypervigilant. This trauma-related symptom of scanning one's environment for signs of danger, or "waiting for the other shoe to drop," is not only a phenomenon of war, but also something that can happen to us when we undergo shocking, or stressful experiences and we don't do anything to ameliorate the effects of them. Italians understand the need to sing to each other in order to engage with others, feel support and gain inspiration. All of these are ways of regulating our anxiety, of down-regulating stress. Learning techniques of self-soothing can allow us to actually reset our basal ganglia so that all the functions that fall under its jurisdiction become more regulated as well. We can learn to process and regulate emotion, to modulate intense feelings that are overwhelming us and develop skills of self-soothing and self-regulation. We want to develop the ability sit with emotions and become able to tolerate and process them rather than run from, numb out or self-medicate.

We also want to remain calm enough through mindful breath awareness, so that the thinking mind can come back on board and "witness" or "observe" the inner workings of our mind. When we can witness without judgement or interference, a clearer picture begins to form almost on its own. Rather than through strain, our own truth emerges organically. And as it does, we gain insight and the thinking mind can make meaning of the circumstances and events of our lives relative to us. In this way we naturally find meaning and a felt sense of purpose can have a chance to surface and make itself known to us.

Another thing we want to accomplish through guided imagery is to consciously turn our negative "forecasting" imaging or thinking, into more positive "forecasting." Because emotions are physical, processed by the body's the limbic system, they make us want to do something, to take an action. If we're scared or angry and cannot take any action because our situation prevents us from it, those stress chemicals cannot be released through action and remain inside of us. Stress is hard on the body and can contribute to anything from brittle hair and nails to heart problems. Guided imagery helps to reduce stress and regulate heart rhythms, which in turn, regulate blood flow to all organs in the body.

How Coloring Mandalas Reduces Anxiety

Coloring Mandalas and listening to guided imageries are two easy and enjoyable "go to's" that research has found do a lot to reduce anxiety.

Coloring is one of the easiest ways to calm yourself at home. Families can do it together and share a moment of pleasure, friends or siblings can sit around, share colored pencils and show each other their creations or coloring can be a meditative way to enjoy some "me time." "A group of researchers at the University of the West of England in Bristol, UK…found that, compared to reading, coloring reduced anxiety and improved mindfulness, as measured by the Mindful Attention Awareness Scale. This finding is not only encouraging for people who want to justify their coloring hobby, but it also validates the use of coloring books in therapy settings. The researchers suggest, for example, that university well-being centers might consider keeping coloring books on hand to support students who come to them with anxiety issues, or that coloring pages could be used as entry-level activities for people who are starting art therapy." (Eva Amsen, Science, 2019). During our COVID-19 days coloring can be an ideal way to turn our brains off and enter a state researchers call "flow." (Journal of the American Art Therapy Association, 22(2) pp. 81–85 © AATA, Inc. 2005)

"Coloring the symmetrical form of the mandala with its repeating patterns and complexity purportedly helps to draw individuals into a state similar to meditation…it combines elements of art therapy (i.e., coloring a form) and meditation (i.e., deeply concentrating on an experience that is soothing). Several authors have documented the effectiveness of art therapy in the treatment of anxiety. Grossman (1981), for example, held that art therapy can help to organize and calm the "inner chaos" that is anxiety because one is allowed to make sense of the confusion of daily life and to communicate without having to find the perfect words."

It's also a go to, to occupy those in confinement, quarantine or treatment programs. In these COVID-19 days when staff may be low and home time may benefit from more creative, calm time, coloring is both an anxiety reducer and a mood elevator that can be enjoyed along or in company!

These activities can be equally helpful doing them on your own or with others. So enjoy coloring the mandalas in this book, relax, let go then find a very comfortable spot to lie back and listen to a guided imagery. These are some ways to turn home into a safe haven and to create a sense of comfort, safety and support within.

Be well, stay safe, "this too, shall pass!"

References

Amen, Daniel: Change Your Brain Change Your Life, Harmony; Revised, Expanded edition (November 3, 2015)

Robert F. Anda, Vincent J. Felitti, David Brown, Daniel Chapman, Maxia Dong, Shanta R. Dube, Valeria Edwards, and Wayne Giles. "Insights into Intimate Partner Violence from the Adverse Childhood Experiences (ACE) Study." In *The Physician's Guide to Intimate Partner Violence and Abuse,* 77–88. 2nd ed. Volcano, CA: Volcano Press, 2006.

Anda, Robert F., Vincent J. Felitti, J. Douglas Bremner, John D. Walker, Charles Whitfield, Bruce D. Perry, Shanta R. Dube, and Wayne H. Giles. "The Enduring Effects of Abuse and Related Adverse Experiences in Childhood." *European Archives of Psychiatry and Clinical Neuroscience* 256, no. 3 (2005): 174–86.

Anda, Robert F., MD, MS, and Vincent J. Felitti, MD. "ACE Reporter: Origins and Essence of the Study." (2003). http://thecrimereport.s3.amazonaws.com/2/94/9/3076/acestudy.pdf.

Bailey, Regina. "Amygdala's Location and Function." Thought Co. (2019). Accessed July 18, 2019. https://www.thoughtco.com/amygdala-anatomy-373211.

Carpi, John. "Stress: It's Worse Than You Think." Psychology Today (1996). Accessed July 25, 2016. https://www.psychologytoday.com/us/articles/199601/stress-its-worse-you-think.

J Collicutt McGrath, PA Linley - Brain Injury, 2006—informahealthcare.com. Journal of Traumatic Stress 2004; 17: 11–21. Tedeschi R, Calhoun L. Posttraumatic growth:

Curry Nancy A. and Kasser, Tim "Can Coloring Mandalas Reduce Anxiety? Galesburg, IL Art Therapy: Journal of the American Art Therapy Association, 22(2) pp. 81–85 © AATA, Inc. 2005

Dayton, Tian. *The Soulful Journey of Recovery: A Guide to Healing from a Traumatic Past for ACA, Codependents or Those With Adverse Childhood Experiences.* 1st ed. Deerfield Beach, FL: Health Communications, 2019.

Dayton, Tian. *Emotional Sobriety: From Relationship Trauma to Resilience and Balance*. 1st ed. Deerfield Beach, FL: Health Communications, 2007.

Felitti, Vincent J., Robert F. Anda, Dale Nordenberg, David F. Williamson, Alison M. Spitz, Valerie Edwards, Mary P. Koss, and James S. Marks. "Relationship of Childhood Abuse and Household Dysfunction to Many of the Leading Causes of Death in Adults: The Adverse Childhood Experiences (ACE) Study." *American Journal of Preventive Medicine* 14, no. 4 (1998): 245–58.

Grant, Jon E., Marc N. Potenza, Aviv Weinstein, and David A. Gorelick. "Introduction to Behavioral Addictions." *The American Journal of Drug and Alcohol Abuse* 36, no. 5 (2010): 233–41.

Hagedorn, W. Bryce. "The Call for a New Diagnostic and Statistical Manual of Mental Disorders Diagnosis: Addictive Disorders." *Journal of Addictions & Offender Counseling* 29, no. 2 (2009): 110–27.

Ireland, Tom. "What Does Mindfulness Meditation Do to Your Brain?" *Scientific American*, 2014.

National Scientific Council on the Developing Child. "Supportive Relationships and Active Skill-Building Strengthen the Foundations of Resilience." *Working Paper* 13 (2015). http://www.developingchild.harvard.edu

Wong, Paul. *The Human Quest for Meaning: Theories, Research, and Applications* (2nd Edition). New York, NY: Routledge, 2012.

Wong, Paul, and Lilian C. J. Wong. "A Meaning-Centered Approach to Building Youth Resilience." Dr. Paul Wong. 2018.

Van der Kolk, B. 1987. *Psychological Trauma*. Washington, D.C.: American Psychiatric Press.

Van der Kolk, Bessel. "The Politics of Mental Health." Psychotherapy Excellence. 2019. https://www.psychotherapyexcellence.com/Blog/2019/May/The-Politics-of-Mental-Health.

Walsh, Bari. "The Science of Resilience." Harvard Graduate School of Education. 2015. https://www.gse.harvard.edu/news/uk/15/03/science-resilience.

Wolin, Steven J. *The Resilient Self: How Survivors of Troubled Families Rise Above Adversity*. NY: Villard Books, 1993.

Reading to Accompany RTR

Emotional Sobriety

From Relationship Trauma to Resilience and Balance

Read the book that this model is based on. With up-to-date research, case studies and readable prose *Emotional Sobriety* will help you understand what happened to you and how to move from relationship trauma to resilience and balance in your own life. It will also guide you through the theoretical, research, and personal underpinnings of the model.

The Soulful Journey of Recovery

A Guide to Healing from a Traumatic Past for ACAs, Codependents, or Those with Adverse Childhood Experiences

More than just a book full of the latest information, this is a dynamic, interactive, and personalized journey of recovery for those impacted by adverse childhood experiences (ACES). Finally, they can put their past behind them where it belongs!

For those who have grown up in a family with addiction, mental illness, or other adverse childhood experiences (ACES), the heartache and pain doesn't end when they grow up and leave home. The legacy can last a lifetime and spread to generations unseen, as author Janet Woititz first showed readers in the groundbreaking *Adult Children of Alcoholics*. In *The ACoA Trauma Syndrome* Dr. Tian Dayton picked up where Dr. Woititz left off, filling in the decades of research that tell us *why* pain from yesterday recreates itself over and over again in our today. In *The Soulful Journey of Recovery,* Dr. Dayton gives us the *how*. Some books can change your life. This is one of them.

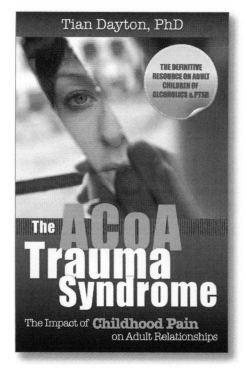

The ACOA Trauma Syndrome
The Impact of Childhood Pain on Adult Relationships

Growing up in a home where there is addiction or relationship trauma puts a child at great risk for long-term, post-traumatic stress effects that adversely compromise adult relationships. Bestselling author, psychologist, and psychodramatist Tian Dayton examines this trauma through an exploration of the way the brain and body process frightening or painful emotions and experiences in childhood, and she shows how these traumas can become catalysts for unhealthy, self-medicating behaviors including drug and alcohol abuse, food issues, and sex, gambling, and shopping addictions.

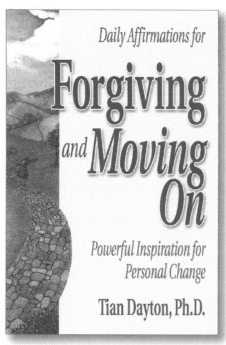

Daily Affirmations for Forgiving and Moving On
Powerful Inspiration for Personal Change

There is a point in our lives when we seem to stand in the center of our own decision about who we are and how we want to be. It comes after enough of the past pain, resentment and grief have been spent, enough deep holes and yearnings have been filled, enough baggage from the past has been dealt with. Now that we've restored ourselves to a "good enough" status, we're ready to meet life more or less as it is happening.

At this point we need to recognize which attitudes and behavior patterns will serve us throughout the rest of our lives and which need to be let go. Can the lives we have envisioned for ourselves flourish under the weight of carried resentment from the past? What does it cost us in terms of happiness and well-being to hang on to the blame and hurt?

Made in the USA
Las Vegas, NV
06 February 2021